*Foundations of
Science and
Mathematics*

Foundations of
Science and
Mathematics

By
Mortimer J. Adler
and
Peter Wolff

Preface by
Curtis Wilson, Former Dean
St. John's College, Annapolis, Maryland

ENCYCLOPÆDIA BRITANNICA, INC.

WILLIAM BENTON
Publisher

Chicago • London • Toronto • Geneva • Sydney • Tokyo • Manila

PREFACE

The present Reading Plan proposes a path to liberal education in science. The role of modern science in liberal education is the subject of widespread and intensive discussion. What should that role be?

Decade by decade, the pace of research in the physical and biophysical sciences is accelerating; and decade by decade, the picture of the world which results from such research becomes stranger, more esoteric, more complicated. There is even a certain justification in saying that the picture becomes less and less a picture, less and less an imaginable model of what is, and more a set of complicated mathematical formulas connected with a set of complicated procedures for getting results.

Meanwhile the results, and the pace at which the results come in, have become matters of political and economic urgency. It is widely recognized that more and more scientists, engineers, and technicians must be trained; that more and more time, cash, patience, and imagination have to be put in the service of scientific development. What is ultimately at stake is the survival of national communities adhering to the principles of democracy and free inquiry.

Lack of immediate intelligibility in science itself and the urgency of continued and accelerated scientific development—these are probably the principal facts which confront the non-scientist when he thinks about science. Both facts present themselves as external, hard necessities; neither fact, the nonscientist may be inclined to add, seems to touch the nerve of our lives.

The present Reading Plan has an aim quite different from any that these facts are likely to suggest. It does not try to bring the layman up to date in science, nor try to help meet the national emergency. Important as these aims are, we have to say that liberal education has an aim which is essentially different and which must claim an ultimate priority.

The classical statement about liberal education is in Book VII of Plato's *Republic*. There Socrates tells Glaucon why the future rulers of the best state must be required to study mathematics: "I am amused, I said, at your fear of the world, which makes you guard against the appearance of insisting upon useless studies; and I quite admit the difficulty of believing that in every man there is an eye of the soul which, when by other pursuits lost and dimmed, is by these purified and re-illumined; and is more precious far than ten thousand bodily eyes, for by it alone is truth seen."

Socrates does not deny the practical utility of mathematics, although he could not have dreamed of the modern mathematical science of nature, or of the continuous transformation of our lives which it effects with ever-increasing speed. Nor is it possible to deny today that a better understanding of science by those in positions of authority and responsibility, as well as by those who shape opinion, would be immensely practical, and would strengthen those rational elements in our civic life which make for orderly development of a free society. But what Socrates is pointing out is what has always been recognized in the Western tradition, whether tacitly or explicitly, as the central aim of liberal education: the freeing of the mind through the discipline of wonder. A plan of education is liberal just insofar as it recognizes the centrality of this aim.

One requirement of liberal education in science should thus be clear. Liberal learning in the sciences is primarily concerned neither with the factual data uncovered by science nor with the hypotheses and theories which form its body; it is rather concerned with the artifices of the human mind and

hand which help us to transcend the factual by reducing it to
universal principles. Information is necessary but not sufficient; the mind must be encouraged and guided to think
through to the roots of scientific ideas.

The present Reading Plan provides an introduction to nine
major works of the scientific revolution of the sixteenth, seventeenth, and eighteenth centuries, as well as to five ancient
works which were among the sources from which that revolution stemmed. The study and exploration of these works are
no mere antiquarian ventures. They lead us back to the roots
of the present-day concepts and hypotheses of science.

Present-day science has a branched and storied structure,
and every scientific concept contains within it sedimented
layers of meaning. If we consider, for instance, the concept
of the electron and seek its meaning, we are led back to
Faraday's investigation of electrolysis, and to J. J. Thomson's
study of the deflection of cathode rays acted upon by electric
and magnetic fields. Faraday found that the weight of a metal
deposited in electrolysis is proportional to the amount of
electricity employed, and, in fact, that the amount of electricity required to deposit a given number of atoms of any metal
is always the same or else a small whole-number multiple of
the unit quantity. Since all chemical substances were regarded
as consisting of atoms, he hypothesized that electricity was
also atomic in character, that is, made up of discrete unit
charges. This result depends, then, on the prior development
of an atomic theory of matter, and on the prior development
of means measuring quantity and intensity of electricity. Thomson's study, on the other hand, demonstrated that a cathode
ray, issuing from the negative plate of a vacuum tube and
consisting of negative electric charge, was deflected by electric
and magnetic forces. But what is acted upon by forces must,
according to Newton's laws, have mass; so the unit quantity
of negative electricity acquires a mass and becomes what we
today call the electron. Thomson's result thus depends on the
vast construction which is Newton's *Mathematical Principles
of Natural Philosophy*. To accept the electron as somehow on
a par with and alongside rocks and trees and tables and chairs

is to commit what Alfred North Whitehead calls "the fallacy of misplaced concreteness." To understand the concept is to trace it to its roots in observation, experimentation, and theory-construction—the playful but exacting game of science.

The unearthing of presuppositions and of buried meanings carries us back beyond Newton to the first deductive science of all, the science of geometry, which has its faraway origins in the everyday techniques of the surveyor and the carpenter, and which appears as a full-fledged, pure science—an artful arrangement of assumptions and proofs—in the *Elements* of Euclid. Fundamental to the vast project conceived by the seventeenth-century innovators was the notion of the geome-trization of nature, the notion of nature as a book written in geometrical characters. This notion is a new version of the ancient faith of Pythagoras and Nicomachus in mathematics as the divine science, the science of the eternal patterns in and behind all things.

It is the work of Copernicus which sets the new science on its way. What Copernicus effects is simply a geometrical trans-formation of Ptolemy's planetary system, the interchange of a circle here and there. He does this partly from classical mo-tives, to preserve the principle of uniform circular motion where Ptolemy had been forced to depart from it, and partly to account for otherwise unexplained correlation between the periods of the planetary anomalies and the solar year. But Copernicus' later followers, such as Kepler, find something strangely fascinating in the motion of the earth, which claims their adherence even before there is satisfactory evidence for its truth. Man is now a world traveler, who sees his motions projected into the sky and thus becomes the measure of all things.

The Copernican revolution leaves unsolved problems in its wake. In particular, Copernicus was unable to answer satis-factorily Ptolemaic objections to the motion of the earth. What is required here is a new physics of terrestrial motion; and it is above all Galileo who, working along Archimedean lines, undertakes to fill this need. Kepler seeks to construct a celes-tial mechanics in which material pushes and pulls and divinely imposed harmonies are oddly mixed; and in the course of trying to verify celestial harmonies of number and distance he discovers the three laws of planetary motion. Finally, Newton weaves a single pattern from these diverse threads, a system of the world.

To follow the strands of this scientific development in detail, to trace out the ways in which facts, assumptions, principles, and mathematical proofs interlock, is to engage in the activity of human reason where it has operated with most obvious success. It is also to dispel, in some measure, the apparent unintelligibility of science for the nonscientist. And finally, it is to make an important beginning in the task of recovering our sense of the unity and wonder of the world, and of the human mind which seeks by observation and logic and artifice to comprehend that world.

If the present Reading Plan, with its carefully thought out analyses and questions, helps some persons to realize these aims, it will have amply fulfilled its purpose.

CURTIS WILSON

FOREWORD

I

This Reading Plan deals with problems in the fields of mathematics and physical science. For most readers it is probably a good idea to begin reading in the *Great Books of the Western World* with the plan entitled "A General Introduction to the Great Books." However, it is not necessary to have read the introductory plan, or any other reading plan, before beginning to use this one. Each Reading Plan in the entire series is designed to be used independently of all the others.

How to use the Reading Plan. The Reading Plan contains three major parts: (1) A list of readings; (2) Guides to each of the readings; and (3) Suggestions for additional readings.

1. *The Reading List.* There are fifteen readings. You should take about two weeks for each reading. The length and difficulty of each reading are designed for that period.

2. *The Guides.* These should prove most helpful to the reader of *Great Books of the Western World* who is going it alone, without teacher, discussion leader, or other study aids. The purpose of the guide is to help you get started on an assignment and to make your reading more meaningful to you. Here you will find the highlights of the reading assignment pointed out, often by quotation. Difficult passages are discussed and explained. The structure of the whole book is considered and the individual parts related to it. There is usually some comment on the form and style of the book being studied. Wherever it is relevant, attention is paid to the

background or historical circumstances under which the book was written, but these matters are less important for the books in this Reading Plan than for those in some of the other plans.

Special problems are presented to you, the critical reader, to think about. These problems are not questions that can be answered by repeating what the text has said. The statement of a problem is followed by a brief discussion which illuminates the problem, indicates some of the possible answers, and emphasizes the importance of the question. Some readers will be satisfied simply to read the problems, and to give them some thought. Others may want to write out answers to them. The questions cannot be answered by a mere "yes" or "no," or "true" or "false." Each problem requires real analysis, and several paragraphs or even an essay may be required for the answer. Since there is no "right" answer to these questions, and since their main purpose is to stimulate some thought about the reading matter, you alone will be able to check and judge your answer.

Each guide concludes with a section entitled SELF-TESTING QUESTIONS. This section gives you an opportunity to check the thoroughness of your reading. Here you will find a series of questions about the reading. The questions are factual; the information asked for is found in the reading. The right answer can, therefore, be simply indicated by reference to a page or pages from the reading assignment. In order to give you an opportunity to check yourself, the correct references are given on pages 223-224.

3. *The Additional Readings.* These give you an opportunity to delve more deeply into the subjects treated in this Reading Plan. We have tried especially to recommend classics of science and mathematics, that is, works or parts of works that are on a level with those in the Reading Plan, and contemporary works that will give you some notion of important current problems in the fields of physical science and mathematics and how they are being treated.

II

It is obvious that an attempt to study science and mathematics with the help of *Great Books of the Western World,* but without teachers, without the aid of modern textbooks, and without the opportunity of laboratory experimentation faces special difficulties. Let us make clear, therefore, what we *are* trying to accomplish in this Reading Plan and, at the same time, what we are *not* trying to do. The reader will thus be able to tell what he can and cannot expect to gain from the use of the Reading Plan.

A glance at the reading list shows that the assignments afford a partial survey of the historical development of science. Nevertheless, in this Reading Plan, we are not interested in the history of science as such. The development of science is fascinating; but here we are concerned with the history of science only incidentally. Though *Great Books of the Western World* afford us a good cross-section of important scientific writings, this set of books does not contain anything like a full record of them. The accelerating pace of scientific progress, especially since 1800, has been such that it was possible to include in the set only a fraction of the number of great scientific works. This Reading Plan uses the study of the history of science merely as a means to another end. That end is the study of scientific method and reasoning.

Books have been written, of course, that deal with nothing but scientific method. Some are excellent works. (See, for example, Poincaré's *Science and Hypothesis,* recommended in the Additional Readings.) But for the most part the best way to become acquainted with the methods of science is to read what the great scientists themselves have to say about their discoveries—how they came to make them, how they interpreted them, and by what reasoning they arrived at their conclusions concerning them.

Sometimes, the great scientists comment on their methods, but very often such commentary is lacking. Archimedes has nothing to say about method in his work on the principle of the lever. While Pascal and Newton are more self-conscious about their procedures and make at least a few remarks about the methods they use, it is true in their case also that we learn more from what they do than from what they say about the methods they employ.

"Scientific method" is a catch phrase, covering almost anything that a scientist does. But in this Reading Plan the reader's attention should be focused on a few factors that recur consistently in scientific work. They are (1) the role of experiment and observation, (2) the method of induction, and (3) the role of hypothesis. We shall briefly comment on each of these three in order to give the reader a better notion of what to look for in the readings he is about to undertake.

1. *Experiment and observation.* These factors are obviously basic to scientific method. The following questions, all of which are raised in the guides to the readings, reveal some of the problems involved.

What is the difference between experiment and observation? Are there any sciences that rely exclusively on the one or on the other of these? What is a controlled experiment? In such an experiment, who controls what?

Are experiments or observations necessary in all sciences? What is the role of common sense and common experience? What is the importance of measurement in an experiment? Does the application of mathematics to experimental findings always depend on the making of measurements?

Are experiment and observation based on theories of causation? Do they involve theories of probability? Does an experiment ever prove anything? Does it ever disprove anything?

2. *Induction.* In general, this term refers to the process whereby from one or a few instances a general law of nature is derived. Some kind of induction, therefore, must be involved in the discovery of any law of nature, whether it is Archimedes' law of the lever or Newton's law of universal gravitation.

The subject of induction is notoriously beset with thorny problems. Here are some of them. Is induction a valid process of acquiring knowledge? Is it a process of logical reasoning or merely a happy propensity of the human mind? Does it lead to "universal laws" or merely to "probable generalizations"?

Does the number of experiments performed increase the probability of an inductive generalization? Is the law relating to the fall of heavy bodies more firmly established now than it was in Newton's time because of the additional times that heavy bodies have been observed to fall?

Does the inductive process need justification? If so, what is involved in its justification? Is it possible to do? What is the role of a "crucial experiment" in inductive reasoning?

3. *Hypothesis.* This term refers to tentative formulations that are made to explain experimental facts. Hypothesis, induction, and experimentation and observation usually occur together in any scientific inquiry. They cannot easily be kept separate. All experimentation and observation is based, to a certain extent, on the experimenter's hypothesis about what he will find; and induction often results in the verification of a hypothesis. Some of the questions about hypotheses that the reader should ask himself are as follows.

Does scientific work always involve hypotheses, or only sometimes? What does it mean to verify a hypothesis? At what point does a hypothesis arise? Is it possible to have different hypotheses concerning the same set of facts? How does one decide in favor of one rather than another hypothesis? Are natural laws hypotheses? Does the use of hypotheses in science throw doubt on the validity of scientific conclusions?

These and similar questions concerning scientific method will be relevant to all the readings in the Plan, and the reader who keeps them in mind as he studies the assignments will be able to derive the maximum benefit from the readings.

III

There are other questions which we should keep in mind for the purely mathematical readings, such as Euclid's *Elements*. In these books, too, we are interested in method more than in content, but the method and the questions that arise concerning it are different. A sampling follows.

What is a mathematical demonstration? What is the logical relationship between the different parts of a mathematical proof? What is an axiom? Can there be more than one correct way of proving a mathematical proposition? Is a mathematical proposition, if demonstrated, necessarily true?

Do geometrical propositions require diagrams for the proof? What is the role of definitions in mathematical proof? Is mathematics based on common sense? How is mathematics applicable to natural phenomena?

IV

A few words remain to be said about what we are *not* trying to accomplish in this Reading Plan. Full realization of this may save the reader some disappointment. We are not trying to give the reader the fundamental facts in the sciences of astronomy, physics, or chemistry. Nor are we attempting to give the reader a brief course in geometry, or in any other branch of mathematics.

The reasons for our inability to teach the content of a science should be obvious. Sciences like physics and chemistry have become so complex and progress in them has become so rapid that even the greatest of the great scientific books have been left far behind. This does not mean that everything contained in the great books of science is false; many of the discoveries of the great scientists are still valid. Archimedes' law of the lever and Galileo's law of falling bodies are still found in any physics textbook, but much has been added to scientific knowledge beyond these laws. And, of course, there are some theories and statements in the older scientific works that are now known to be false.

Falsity is not a problem in the mathematical works. The truths demonstrated by the ancients are still acknowledged to be true. But modern mathematical theory has developed far beyond the ancients. From the modern point of view, Euclid, for example, is at best a very incomplete exposition of geometry.

What remains worth studying are exactly those things to which we propose to pay attention in this Reading Plan: the methods which the scientist and the mathematician employ. These methods, together with reflections concerning the nature of physical science and mathematics, constitute the primary subject matter of the assignments to follow. Attention will also necessarily be paid to the discoveries of the scientists, since we cannot understand their methods except in the context of the discoveries they made by their use.

CONTENTS

A NOTE ON
REFERENCE STYLE

In referring to *Great Books* the same style is used as in the *Syntopicon*. Pages are cited by number and section. In books that are printed in single column, "a" and "b" refer to the upper and lower half of the page. In books that are printed in double column, "a" and "b" refer to the upper and lower half of the left column, "c" and "d" to the upper and lower half of the right column. For example, "Vol. 53, p. 210b" refers to the lower half of page 210, since Vol. 53, James's *Principles of Psychology*, is printed in single column. But "Vol. 7, p. 202b" refers to the lower left quarter of page 202, since Vol. 7, Plato's *Dialogues*, is printed in double column.

THE READING LIST

EUCLID

Elements

Book I

Definitions, Postulates, Common Notions, Prop. 1–26

Vol. 11, pp. 1–17

Geometry is the study of the mathematical properties of space. It investigates certain qualities of figures such as size, shape, distance, and congruence (equality).

At first glance, this may seem abstract and irrelevant to human concerns, without any relation to concrete existence. But if we think a bit, we see that this is simply not true, for geometry has something to say about anything that exists or can exist in space. The word itself, meaning "earth measurement," indicates the quite earthy and practical origin of the science in ancient Egypt and Babylonia. The Greeks developed this early empirical study into the abstract, demonstrative science which most of us studied in high school.

Euclid's *Elements* is the fruit of this development. It is the classic textbook of Greek geometry, which has served as the basis of study for over twenty centuries. It is a model of clear and orderly presentation. The *Elements* is really elementary. It has the classic simplicity and order that so often characterize a great work which summarizes generations or centuries of study.

You do not have to be a mathematical wizard in order to follow Euclid. Normal intelligence and close attention are all that is needed to learn or relearn the elements of Euclidean geometry.

I

In reading Book I of Euclid's *Elements,* which has an intricate structure involving 23 definitions, 5 postulates, 5 common notions, and 48 propositions, one can easily lose sight of the whole, or perhaps, never even succeed in seeing the whole at all. The sense of unity is further diminished by the fact that the reader is not likely to read the book through quickly.

Our first effort, therefore, will be to indicate the sense in which Book I of the *Elements* is a meaningful whole. The reader can help himself to see the structure and unity of Book I by leafing through it and getting a general idea of its contents. This need not involve a detailed reading of the proofs of the propositions, but only a glance at the propositions themselves and at the accompanying diagrams.

If we wished to give a title to this first book, we might well call it "Concerning Triangles and Parallelograms." These two kinds of figures are the main subjects discussed. A few other matters are touched on, but only in an incidental way.

The book can roughly be divided as follows. Propositions 1-26 deal with triangles; Propositions 27-32, with parallel lines; and Propositions 33-48, with parallelograms. The middle series of propositions, numbers 27-32, provides the transition from triangles to parallelograms. Their transitional character does not lessen the importance of these propositions. On the contrary, the theory of parallel lines is among the most important contributions of Euclid.

Another way of grasping the unity of these 48 propositions consists in realizing what is *not* here. In general, the subject of Book I is plane geometry, but certain aspects of this subject are not treated by Euclid in Book I. There is, for instance, hardly any mention of circles and their properties; Euclid treats this subject in Book III. A more significant omission is the lack of concern with measurement in Book I. There is occasional reference to the fact that something is greater than something else, but there is no attempt to indicate how much greater. All measurement of quantities involves ratios and proportions. Euclid treats ratios and proportions in Book V of the *Elements,* and geometrical measurement in Book VI. We can further refine our description of the subject of Book I by saying that it is concerned only with the equalities and inequalities of triangles and parallelograms.

II

If we look at Book I in detail, we find that Proposition 1 is preceded by three other sections, entitled "Definitions," "Postulates," and "Common Notions." It is not difficult to see why the definitions are placed first. Before Euclid can tell us anything about triangles, circles, and so on, he must tell us what these objects are. However, there are some difficulties about particular definitions.

Consider the first definition, for instance, "A *point* is that which has no part." Does this definition succeed in telling us what a point is? It gives us some idea of what a point is *not*. For example, it is not a dot, nor a mark on a piece of paper, such as we find in the diagrams accompanying the propositions. Any such physical mark clearly has parts. They may be small, but they are still parts. Anything of any size, no matter how small, can be divided further, and so the only conclusion which we can come to with respect to a point is that it has no size at all. It is *dimensionless.*

But this does not tell us what a point is. On the contrary, the definition seems capable of being interpreted in such a way that a point is nothing. For if I say that a point is something, I always meet the difficulty that anything has parts. Only nothing is without parts. Yet Euclid clearly means to be talking about something that has geometrical reality, not about nothing.

The first definition is not the only one that presents difficulties. The second definition is just as puzzling: "A *line* is breadthless length." Here again the definition serves to disabuse us of any notion which we may have had that a line, as Euclid understands it, is the same as a line drawn with pencil on a piece of paper. Any such line will, of course, have some breadth, no matter how sharp the pencil with which it is drawn. But on the positive side we do not gain much understanding of "line" when we are told that it is length without breadth, or that a line is one-dimensional (just as a point was a non-dimensional).

Definition 4 is also a difficult one to understand: "A *straight line* is a line which lies evenly with the points on itself." The definition may be perfectly adequate. It is, however, not at all clear that "evenly" is any less in need of a definition than "straight."

Other definitions of a straight line are possible. Plato, in the *Parmenides*, gives this definition of it: ". . . the straight is that of which the centre intercepts the view of the extremes." (See Vol. 7, p. 492b). You have also undoubtedly heard a straight line defined as "the shortest distance between two points."

The obscurity of the definitions which we have so far considered, together with the multiplicity of definitions for one and the same thing, points to a general problem about definitions. *Not everything can be defined.* And the attempt to define what can not or need not be defined often results in greater obscurity than there would be if the attempt were not made.

It is easy to see that any science, such as geometry, must begin with certain undefined terms. For any definition of a term always makes use of other terms. Now these terms may themselves be in need of a definition; but if they are defined, their definition will involve still other terms. These terms again will either have a definition, or else they must remain undefined. No matter how many definitions we make, there can be no end to definition-making, unless we are content to leave some terms undefined.

The presence of undefined terms can be detected in the definitions to which we have already called attention. Definition 4—"A *straight line* is a line which lies evenly with the points on itself"—utilizes the terms "line," "point," and "evenly." Now *line* has been defined in Definition 2 as "breadthless length," while *point* was said in Definition 1 to be "that which has no part." But this still leaves "evenly" undefined; furthermore, Definitions 1 and 2 also contain undefined terms. Thus, in Definition 2 we are not told what "length" is, while Definition 1 leaves us in the dark about the notion of "part."

The foregoing suggests the following question. If, in any science, there must always be undefined terms, what criteria determine *which* terms are to be undefined? With respect to Euclid's *Elements*, we can ask more specifically: Did Euclid leave the correct terms undefined, or would some other choice have been better? Would it, for instance, have been just as good—or better—to have left *point* and *line* undefined?

In any case, one conclusion from these considerations is that, if Euclid's work were arranged in a truly systematic fashion, then the section "Definitions" would be preceded by another section entitled "Undefined Terms," which would list such terms as "part," "breadth," "length," "even," "lying on," and many others.

III

The next two sections, "Postulates" and "Common Notions," are very much shorter than the section entitled "Definitions." But they are no less important.

It is perhaps rather easy to understand what common notions are. (They are sometimes also called "axioms.") Looking at the five common notions that Euclid states, we have no trouble in assenting to the truth of the statements. The ease with which their truth is recognized is the special characteristic of common notions. They are self-evident. By this we mean that when the terms involved in their statement are understood, then the truth of the statements is also understood. It might also be pointed out that one of the common notions—about whole and part—reveals to us our intuitive understanding of one of the terms Euclid left undefined.

What are the "postulates"? It is obvious that they are not uniform, but fall into two groups. The first three postulates declare that something is possible or can be done—a straight line can be drawn; it can be extended; and circles can be drawn. The last two postulates, however, are propositions which appear to assert that something is true, namely that all right angles are equal, and that two lines will meet if certain rather complicated conditions are fulfilled. Just because the fifth postulate is so complicated, it has traditionally been the subject of much discussion and the source of much trouble. We shall return to this famous postulate later.

First, however, let us investigate postulates as such. What do they do, and why are they needed? Why, for instance, is it necessary to state that a circle can be drawn with any center and any radius? Is there any doubt about this? Is it not obvious that circles can be drawn?

The reply is that it is not obvious that circles can be drawn. The third postulate, therefore, "demands" from the reader his assent to the geometric possibility of drawing them. To understand the need for the demand, we must remember that the circles Euclid talks about are not circles on a piece of paper. The boundary of a circle is a line, that is, breadthless length; and a circle is a plane figure, which means a figure without thickness. These conditions, drawn from the definitions, assure us that Euclid is not talking about material figures, but rather about certain ideal figures. Consequently, it is irrelevant that there are such things as compasses which enable us to draw visible circles on paper. The circles that Euclid is concerned with do not come into existence with the help of compasses. How, then, *do* Euclid's circles come into existence? The answer is, "by means of the third postulate."

What that postulate demands from us is our assent that, around a given center and with a given radius, a circle can be drawn—not with a compass but with the mind. Nothing but the mind can draw a Euclidean circle.

The same thing holds true for the drawing of straight lines. Euclid is not asking us to believe that more or less straight pencil lines can be drawn on paper with the help of a straightedge. This is an obvious fact of experience. He is asking our assent to the statement that a line in his sense (that is, an ideal line without any thickness) can be drawn between any two points (the points, too, being ideal and thus partless). The instrument which performs this operation is again the mind.

Another way of looking at these first three postulates is that they are Euclid's way of asking us to assume with him that straight lines and circles exist. If he did not postulate that lines and circles exist as ideal figures, the science of geometry would remain entirely hypothetical. All the propositions of geometry would then have to be stated as true only *if* circles and straight lines exist.

The basic point which must be understood here is that the definitions of geometrical objects give us no assurance of their existence. Definitions say *what* these objects are, but fail to show *that* they exist in the ideal space of the geometer. A familiar example of something that can be defined but does not exist is a mermaid. A mermaid is easily defined as half woman-half fish, but there is no reason to think that such an object exists in the world of living organisms, just because it can be defined.

What is the function of the last two postulates? As we have already indicated, they are propositions which resemble the common notions more than they do the first three postulates. But unlike the common notions, they are not self-evident; nor are they—like the 48 propositions in the body of Book I—capable of proof. Postulates 4 and 5 are propositions whose truth Euclid asks the reader to assume. He needs them, but he cannot prove them.

Why does Euclid need to assume the truth of the statements in Postulates 4 and 5? Consider the statement that "all right angles are equal to one another." Definition 10 tells us what a right angle is: "When a straight line set up on a straight line makes the adjacent angles equal to one another, each of the equal angles is *right* . . ." Consider, therefore, a straight line ABC, on which there is another straight line set up, namely the line DB. Let angle ABD = angle DBC. Then, according to the definition, each

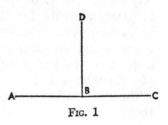

FIG. 1

of the angles ABD, DBC is a right angle. Now let there be a straight line EFG. Let another straight line be set up on it, namely line FH. And let the angle EFH = angle HFG. Then, according to the same definition, each of the angles EFH and HFG is also a right angle. But can we prove that, for example, angle ABD = angle EFH? There is no way of doing it without Postulate 4.

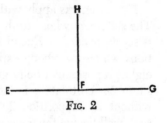

FIG. 2

And with the postulate, no proof is necessary.

Postulate 4 may be interpreted as asserting the homogeneity of geometrical space. It asserts that right angles are equal, wherever they are found in space. A right angle remains a right angle even if it is moved about. As long as the two lines whose intersection forms the right angles remain such that the adjacent angles are equal, they may be moved back and forth while the right angles retain their same size. (We shall return to this point in the Guide to the Second Reading.)

Without Postulate 4, Euclid's entire work would not collapse. It would, however, be a different work from what it is. If we examine the propositions in Book I, we find that Postulate 4 is not used until Proposition 14. All the propositions prior to 14, therefore, can be proved without the use of Postulate 4. But none of the propositions coming after 14 can be proved without it. A geometry might be imagined, therefore, which did not use Postulate 4. Its beginnings (Propositions 1-13) would be exactly the same as Euclid's; but thereafter a very different series of propositions would be proved in our imaginary geometry. For the most part, the difference would be on the side of omissions. For instance, our imaginary geometry could not prove that if two straight lines intersect, then the vertical angles formed by the intersection are equal. (See *Elements*, I, 15.)

The last remark indicates the sense in which Euclid "needs" Postulate 4. It is useful in order to prove a whole host of propositions—such as the one about the equality of vertical angles—which common sense expects to be proved in a geometry. A geometry which did not contain these propositions would be accounted odd.

These remarks apply with even greater force to Postulate 5. The statement whose truth we are asked to assume is one that is sorely needed if Euclid is to prove a great many propositions which everybody expects to have proved. For twenty-eight propositions Euclid gets along without it, but in Proposition 29, Postulate 5 is introduced. It is indispensable here; without it, Proposition 29 cannot be proved. Furthermore, such well-known theorems as that the sum of the angles of any triangle is equal to two right angles cannot be proved without Proposition 29, and, therefore, cannot be proved without Postulate 5.

A remarkable difference between Postulates 4 and 5 is evident, however. Postulate 4 is simple and almost everyone is willing to grant it; indeed, there is some difficulty in seeing that it *is* a postulate and not a self-evident truth. Postulate 5, on the other hand, is complex; it includes a number of conditions and then states a conclusion. Postulate 5 has always seemed so much like a proposition which should be demonstrable that any number of attempts have been made to prove its truth, with the help of the first four postulates, the common notions, and the first 28 propositions of Book I. All such attempts have failed. Postulate 5 is needed, if we wish to prove the remaining propositions in Book I, but its validity must be assumed.

We can understand a little better that this postulate is a bare assumption if we realize that other and contrary assumptions can take its place.

To illustrate this, let us state Postulate 5 in a different but equivalent form: Given a straight line and a point outside that line, then only one line not meeting the given line can be constructed (in the plane of the given line and point). That is, given line AB and the point C, one and only one line can be drawn through C not meeting AB.

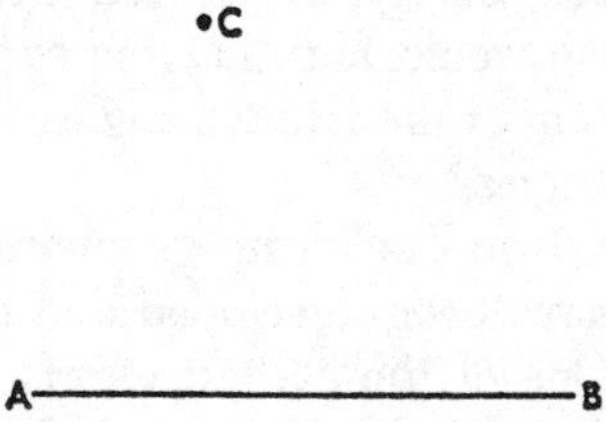

•C

A————————————————————B

FIG. 3

It would be easy to show that this version of Postulate 5 is equivalent to Euclid's. For instance, the truth of Proposition 29 can be proved by means of this postulate as well as by Euclid's.

Now, however, let us imagine that some geometer other than Euclid were to come along and, instead of Postulate 5, were to state the following. Postulate 5a: Given a straight line and a point outside that line, then an infinite number of straight lines not meeting the given line can be drawn through the given point. That is, given the line AB and the point C, any number of lines like DCE,

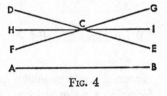

FIG. 4

FCG, HCI, etc., can be drawn, none of them meeting the original line AB.

It takes some effort of the imagination to think of this as possible. But since neither Postulate 5 nor Postulate 5a are *true*, both being mere *assumptions*, it is only habit that inclines us to favor the Euclidean postulate.

Another possible postulate contrary to both 5 and 5a would be this. Postulate 5b: Given a straight line and a point not on that line, no line can be drawn through that point that does not meet the given line. A briefer way of saying this is that there are no parallel lines.

What results do we get if we substitute Postulates 5a or 5b

for Euclid's Postulate 5? Using either of the substitutes, a consistent geometrical system can be developed. These are systems different from Euclid's geometry, though having certain resemblances to it. For instance, using Postulate 5a, we can prove the proposition that the sum of the interior angles of a triangle is less than two right angles. Using Postulate 5b, we would find that the corresponding proposition is that the sum of the interior angles of a triangle is more than two right angles.

Non-Euclidean geometries, using Postulates 5a and 5b, have been developed and have been shown to be consistent. One of the earliest efforts in this direction is the *Theory of Parallels* by Nicholas Lobachevski, published in 1840. Using Postulate 5a (that through any point there is an infinite number of lines not intersecting a given line), he develops—in a fashion quite similar to Euclid's—a series of propositions not to be found in Euclid, such as the one that the sum of the interior angles of a triangle is less than two right angles. Other works on non-Euclidean geometry are listed in the Additional Readings to this Plan.

IV

Why does Euclid begin Book I with Propositions 1-3?

Propositions in geometry are of two kinds: (1) the statement of problems in the construction of figures, and (2) theorems or statements of the relations between figures or their parts.

Construction propositions require that something be done; theorems require that something be proved. Accordingly, we find that at the end of Proposition 1, which is a construction proposition, Euclid puts the phrase "(Being) what it was required to do." In later construction propositions, this phrase is replaced by the three letters "Q.E.F." This abbreviation stands for the Latin phrase *Quod erat faciendum,* which means the same as the English phrase.

Similarly, at the end of Proposition 4, which is a theorem, Euclid puts the phrase "(Being) what it was required to prove." In later theorems this phrase is replaced by the letters "Q.E.D." Again these letters stand for the equivalent Latin phrase, *Quod erat demonstrandum.*

The first three propositions, it will be noted, are all problems of construction. The first theorem is Proposition 4. No reference is made in Proposition 4 to the three earlier propositions. Thus, as far as the systematic order of the book goes, it appears that Euclid could have started with Proposition 4 and introduced the three constructions later.

But is there any advantage to his having started out with the three constructions? And what is the general purpose of construction? One answer is readily at hand: the constructions are needed in the proofs of the theorems. This is not apparent in the first four propositions, but we can see it in the fifth proposition. This is a theorem. It states that in an isosceles triangle (a triangle with two equal sides) the base angles are equal. This involves the use of Proposition 3, for a shorter line is cut off from a longer line. Since Proposition 3, in turn, depends on the use of the construction in Proposition 2, while Proposition 2 involves Proposition 1, we see that these three constructions are needed for the sake of Proposition 5.

Constructions can also be interpreted as serving another purpose. They bear an obvious similarity to the first three postulates. Both constructions and postulates assert that certain geometrical operations can be performed. In the case of the postulates, the possibility is assumed; in the case of the propositions, it is proved. The proof involves, of course, the use of the postulates. Just as the postulates can be interpreted as stating the assumption that straight lines and circles *exist* (to say that they can be drawn is to say that they have geometrical reality), so the construction propositions can be interpreted as showing that other geometrical entities exist. Thus we might wonder whether there is really such a thing as an equilateral triangle, defined in Definition 20. Proposition 1 shows that from the assumption that straight lines and circles exist, it follows that equilateral triangles exist.

Construction propositions are, therefore, sometimes referred to as existence propositions. Incidentally, note that there is no postulate asserting the existence of a point. Is this a serious omission on Euclid's part?

Is there any need for Proposition 2?

Let there be point A, and let there be a finite straight line BC. The problem of Proposition 2 is to construct a straight line, starting at A, that is equal in length to BC. In the diagram accompanying the proposition, that line turns out to be AL.

But is it necessary to go through the various steps of the construction? Why can we not simply appeal to Postulate 3 ("to describe a circle with any centre and distance") and say: "With A as center, and radius equal to BC, describe a circle." Any of the radii of this circle will then fulfill the requirements of starting at A and being equal to BC.

In Euclid's view, the difficulty is that the line BC is not at A. In order for a circle to be drawn with A as center and with a radius of "any distance," that distance must start from A. Thus, this construction may be described as a series of maneuvers by which distances are moved around from point to point, in order that circles may be drawn. The parts of the construction may be outlined as follows.

First, the equilateral triangle ABD is constructed. This yields the point D.

Secondly, DB is extended indefinitely and a circle described with B as center and BC as distance. This circle cuts DB extended in point G. This yields us the distance DG.

Thirdly, AD is extended indefinitely and a circle is described with D as center and DG as distance. This circle cuts AD extended in L. AL is the required line.

In the series of steps, we have indicated that the first one "yields" point D and the second one "yields" distance DG. By this we mean that the steps are taken just for the sake of these results. Once Euclid has a center (D) and a distance starting at that center (DG), he can draw a circle, according to Postulate 3. Having drawn the circle, all that remains to do is to show that the line AL, determined by the circle, is the line we are looking for.

After the construction called for in Proposition 2 has been shown to be possible, Euclid is then entitled to do the very thing we suggested he might have done earlier. Now that he has shown us how to place any given line at a given point, he can draw a circle around a point X with any distance QP, even though QP does not start at X. For he can always point out that by Proposition 2 he can place QP so that it (or its equivalent in length) starts at X, and then a circle can be drawn.

Euclid's achievement can also be summarized in this way. Postulate 3 asserts or assumes the possibility that, given point Y and the distance YR, a circle may be drawn. Proposition 2 adds to this by showing that, given point X and the distance PQ, a circle may be drawn around X with PQ as distance. After Proposition 2, in other words, we no longer need to

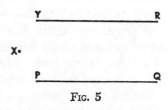

Fig. 5

have the "distance" start at the center of the circle in order to draw a circle with the distance as radius. This proposition illustrates the Euclidean procedure in general: with each succeeding proposition, Euclid becomes less and less limited; he can make more and more constructions and can appeal to more and more geometrical truths.

What are the various parts of a Euclidean proof?

Let us investigate this question using Proposition 5 as an example. The proposition is: "In isosceles triangles, the angles at the base are equal to one another." (Euclid's proposition actually contains more, but this is the essential portion of it.) This way of stating the proposition does not make it quite clear what is to be proved. The following restatement is better: "If a triangle is isosceles, then the angles at the base are equal to one another."

The "if" clause contains that which is *given*, what we have to work with. It is often called the hypothesis. The "then" clause states the conclusion of the proposition. The course of the proof consists in going from what is given, by a series of steps, to the conclusion. The steps are made possible by the postulates and axioms, as well as by previously proved propositions.

In Proposition 5, what is given is an isosceles triangle. The conclusion is that the angles at the base are equal. The intermediate steps use, as a glance at the proof shows, Postulates 1 and 2, and Propositions 3 and 4.

When the conclusion has been reached, the proposition has been proved. It has then been shown that if something is true (namely the hypothesis), and if some additional things are valid (the definitions, axioms, postulates, or prior propositions), then something else is also true, namely the conclusion. The proposition asserts this if-then relationship. It does not assert the truth of the hypothesis, nor does it assert the truth of the conclusion, except when the hypothesis is true. Nor is this connection between hypothesis and conclusion seen to be true until the proposition is proved. It is precisely the truth of this connection that is proved.

What is the logical relation between the hypothesis, the added steps, and the conclusion? Are the earlier steps logical premises for the later steps? Is the "given" a premise in the proof? Is the logic here employed the same as the logic in a typical syllogism, such as this one:

All animals are mortal;
All men are animals;
Therefore: all men are mortal.

Or is the logical process employed different from this?

Is the diagram, present in every Euclidean proposition, also an integral part of the proof? Or is it merely an aid to the imagination of the reader? Could the proposition be proved without it?

The following questions are designed to help you test the thoroughness of your reading. Each question is to be answered by giving a page or pages of the reading assignment. Answers will be found on page 223 of this Reading Plan.

1 What are the congruence propositions in Book I (the propositions showing under what conditions two triangles are equal)?

2 What is the relation of the exterior angle of a triangle to the interior angles?

3 What is a circle?

4 Which proposition establishes that "a straight line is the shortest distance between two points"?

5 What are all the propositions and postulates on which Proposition 9 is directly dependent?

6 Can a triangle be constructed out of any three straight lines?

17

EUCLID

Elements

Book I

Prop. 27–48

Vol. 11, pp. 17–29

Euclid teaches us not only the elementary propositions of geometry; he also teaches us what the geometrical method is. If you are new to the subject of geometry, you might think that any proof is just like any other. But this is not so.

Euclid shows real artistry in inventing different types of proof and choosing the right one for a proposition. Almost always his proofs are simple, clear, and elegant. Instinctively, he seems to know which of a set of alternate proofs is the one he ought to use.

The genius of the poet has sometimes been opposed to that of the mathematician. Blaise Pascal, himself an extraordinarily gifted mathematician, begins his *Pensées* by discussing "the difference between the mathematical and the intuitive mind." And yet it seems that Euclid oftentimes knows intuitively what to do next in a proof and what will persuade the reader. As the poet knows that *this* is the right word in this verse, so Euclid knows that *this* is the way in which to prove this proposition.

He skilfully juggles all the means at his disposal. Sometimes he employs constructions; sometimes he does not. Sometimes he moves his figures through space and sets one on top of another. Sometimes even absurdity is enlisted on the side of reason and used to prove something.

Euclid is indefatigable in using his imagination and skill. When you remember that here we read only one book of the *Elements,* out of a total of thirteen books, you will understand why the name Euclid has always been synonymous with "geometer."

Second Reading

I

Just as it was not possible to confine the previous guide to a discussion of the first 26 propositions, so here we will not be able to avoid references to the beginning of Book I. This is due not only to the fact that both readings are from Book I and that Book I is a unit, but also to the further fact that there is a definite order in the *Elements*. That order is progressive. Each proposition rests on earlier ones; piece by piece, the whole book is put together. Since, then, later propositions rest on earlier ones, we cannot discuss Propositions 27-48 without referring to the earlier propositions, as well as the definitions, postulates, and common notions; and since, similarly, the earlier propositions find their fulfillment and culmination in later ones, we could not discuss the first half of the book (Propositions 1-26) without anticipating some of the results of the second half (Propositions 27-48).

Let us first note the subject of the second half of Book I. The first half dealt with triangles, and especially the conditions of congruence—their equality in shape and size. In the Guide to the First Reading, we described Propositions 27-32 as transitional. They deal with properties of parallel lines (Propositions 29 and 30), as well as the conditions of parallelism (Propositions 27 and 28). Proposition 31 teaches us how to draw a line parallel to a given line, and Proposition 32 proves what is perhaps the best-known property of a triangle: that the sum of its angles is equal to two right angles. The proof of this proposition makes it clear—and we have already commented on the fact—that this property is intimately connected with the "parallel postulate."

Beginning with Proposition 33, Euclid turns his attention to parallelograms (which include rectangles and squares). The most important change from the first part of the book, however, does not consist in the fact that parallelograms take the place of triangles, but rather in the fact that Euclid's interest now is in the *areas* of the figures. He is no longer interested in angles, or lengths, or congruence. Propositions 35-41 establish the equivalence of certain areas, while Propositions 42-46 teach us how to construct certain kinds of parallelogrammic areas. Proposition 47, finally, constitutes the climax of Book I (Proposition 48 is nothing but an afterthought): it shows that in a right-angled triangle the square on the side opposite the right angle is equal to the sum of the squares on the other two sides.

II

Proposition 47 of Book I is probably the most celebrated proposition in all of elementary plane geometry. Its discovery is generally ascribed to Pythagoras and legend has it that when he finally came upon the proof of the proposition he sacrificed one hundred oxen to the gods by way of thanksgiving. Whether or not we choose to believe this legend in all particulars, it does disclose one undisputed fact: Euclid himself was not the discoverer of this proposition. The *Elements* is not to be thought of as an entirely original work by Euclid, for Euclid's major task was that of a compiler. He took known geometrical truths and put them together in an orderly and "elementary" fashion.

Other men, in addition to Pythagoras, are mentioned as the discoverers of much of the content of Euclid's *Elements*. The content of Book V, the theory of ratios and proportions, is usually ascribed to Eudoxus. The content of Book X, treating of lines that are incommensurable with one another, is thought to be the work of Theaetetus. (In Plato's dialogue of that name, there is allusion to the young Theaetetus' proficiency in mathematics.)

Euclid's contribution, however, must not be underestimated. A good deal of the content of the thirteen books is no doubt his own, and all of it has been put together by him in a systematic order, so that the entire edifice of Euclidean geometry is built up from a few definitions, postulates, and common notions.

Euclid is also responsible for selecting the propositions to be included in the *Elements* and for omitting others. Many propositions besides those contained in the *Elements* can be proved. Textbooks of geometry list many of them as "original" problems to be solved by the student. The propositions which Euclid chose to include are evidently those which he considered *elementary* in the sense that they are the elements out of which the rest of geometry can be developed. They are the propositions with the help of which all the other propositions can be proved. Just as the definitions, postulates, and axioms are the principles of geometry, needed to prove any proposition, so the propositions proved by Euclid are the elements of geometry, needed to solve all other geometrical problems.

Though Proposition 47 was probably discovered by Pythagoras, there is reason to think that the particular way in which its truth is here demonstrated is Euclid's own contribution. This proposition like most others can be proved in many different ways.

In the very early propositions of Book I, there is little opportunity for alternative proofs, since the geometer has so little to work with. By the end of Book I, however, a great many tools are available, and Euclid's proof is only one among the many that are possible.

We can illustrate this point by giving just one alternative proof for Proposition 47. As a matter of fact, it involves less previous geometrical knowledge than does Euclid's proof. To begin, construct two equal squares, ABCD and EFGH. Next, make AK equal to CL. Draw KM parallel to BC, and LN parallel to AB. Call the point at which KM and LN intersect, O. Join AO, and OC. Now, in the second square make EP equal to AK. Similarly, make FQ, GR, HS, equal to AK or to EP. Join PQRS.

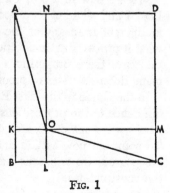

Fig. 1

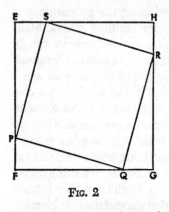

FIG. 2

It can easily be proved that the figure PQRS is a square. Furthermore, it is even clearer that the two figures NOMD and KBLO are squares.

One need only to look at the two figures to see that the square PQRS is equal to the sum of the two squares NOMD and KBLO in the other figure. For PQRS takes up as much space in the second figure as NOMD and KBLO take up in the first figure. We know that they take up the same amount of space when we notice that in both figures the same amount is left over—namely four triangles. And it is easy to prove that the four triangles in Figure 1 are equal to the four triangles in Figure 2. And, finally, the square PQRS is "on" the side opposite the right angle (i.e., PQRS is on the side SP of the right triangle ESP). Again, the square NOMD is on the side NO of the triangle NOA, while square KBLO is on the side OK or NA (since the two are equal) of the triangle NOA. And so the proposition is proved.

III

We are now in a position to look back upon the whole of Book I and all 48 of its propositions. Each of the propositions is different from any of the others in its content, that is, in what it proves. But, in addition, there are many differences in the ways these propositions are proved. Geometry employs many different styles of proof.

In the Guide to the First Reading, we mentioned one major difference in the propositions themselves. Some of the propositions, we pointed out, are *constructions;* others are *theorems.* To point out now certain differences in the way propositions are proved, we will consider only the theorems, and ignore the constructions.

Let us begin by considering Proposition 5. It uses the kind

of proof that most of us have in mind when we think of geometrical method. The proof employs certain auxiliary constructions, and then proceeds to its conclusion, in this case the equality of two angles, by showing that two triangles are congruent, that is, that they have the same size and shape. The use of congruent triangles to prove that lines and angles are equal is a favorite method of Euclid's. It consists in showing that if two triangles are equal in certain specified respects, then they are congruent and, in consequence, we know that they are equal in all other respects.

There is one caution which must be observed with this kind of "typical" proof. Since it involves construction, we must be sure, first, that the construction is possible; and, second, that the construction does not assume the results of the proposition to be proved, for this would make the proof circular. The possibility of the construction in Proposition 5, for instance, must not in any way depend on the base angles' being equal, since that is the very thing to be proved. Many so-called geometrical puzzles or paradoxes are based on constructions which are apparently valid, but which actually violate these rules.

Another very important type of proof is introduced in Proposition 4 and used again in Proposition 8. We may call it by the general name of "superposition." Both Propositions 4 and 8 prove the congruence of two triangles by an imaginary lifting of one triangle and placing it on top of the other triangle. Euclid points out how all the various parts of one triangle fall on top of the corresponding parts of the other one, and thus we see the equality of the two triangles.

Considerable doubt can be raised about the validity of superposition as a proof. Euclid, who is so finicky in Propositions 1-3 about doing no more than his postulates allow, seems strangely ready to superimpose one triangle upon another without any warrant. We are impelled to ask why he did not present us with the following postulate: "A geometrical figure can be moved from place to place without distortion."

This may be the answer: Postulate 2 asserts some degree of

uniformity of space. There is no distortion, it states, when a straight line is extended. Postulate 4 also implies uniformity of space. Since all right angles are equal to one another, there is no distortion in moving a right angle from one position in space to another.

These two postulates together may obviate the need for an explicit postulate which denies that geometrical figures are distorted when they are moved about. Since neither straight lines nor right angles are subject to such distortion, perhaps it follows that no figures made up of lines and angles suffer distortion by motion. In any case, the uniformity of space must be postulated, either explicitly or implicitly, for it is possible to conceive a curved space in which figures shrink, expand, or are otherwise distorted as they are moved about.

In Propositions 4 and 8 Euclid moves the whole triangle at once, not bit by bit. Thus, in Proposition 4, he does not first place one side on top of one side, and then construct an angle at the end of the line. He cannot do this, because he does not yet know how to construct angles. This is done in Proposition 23, which depends on Proposition 8, which, in turn, depends on other propositions that depend on Proposition 4. Such a construction would, therefore, be one of the illegitimate kind we mentioned earlier. Its use would assume the very theorem to be proved.

Another criticism which can be made of the method of superposition is that it is too visual. Our conviction that the two triangles are congruent seems to depend on our looking at the diagrams and convincing ourselves that it really is not possible for one triangle to be placed on top of the other one without complete coincidence. There are, in other words, no logical steps in this proof; nothing but an appeal to intuition. Yet intuition may be a poor guide here.

If it is said, as it may well be, that, though the proof is poor, the theorem is undoubtedly true and vitally needed throughout the rest of the book, then it can be replied that Proposition 4 had better be simply stated as a postulate and accepted as such. It would then be available for use throughout the rest of the book, but it would not be based on a proof of dubious validity, but be clearly and unequivocally stated as an assumption. Certainly, it is no harder to accept than the fifth postulate.

A third kind of proof that is very important in mathematics is the so-called *reduction to the absurd,* or *reduction to the impossible.* Euclid uses it quite frequently. The first time it occurs is in Proposition 6. We next find it in Proposition 7, then in 14, 19, 25, 26, 27, 29, 39, and 40.

This kind of proof takes the following form. Let X stand for proposition to be proved. In order to prove X, we then assume the contradictory of X, namely not-X. Thus, in Proposition 6, where we must prove that AB is equal to AC, we assume the contradictory; namely, that AB is *not* equal to AC. We then see what can be deduced from not-X, together with what is given in the proposition and what we already know from previous propositions.

In Proposition 6, X is the proposition that AB is equal to AC. We assume that not-X is the case or that AB is not equal to AC, and specifically that AB is greater than AC. Euclid then uses Proposition 3, and from AB cuts off a line equal to AC, namely BD. Thus AC = BD. Now Euclid uses Proposition 4 and shows that triangle DBC = triangle ACB. But this result, Euclid says, is absurd, for triangle DBC is totally contained within triangle ACB. Therefore the two cannot possibly be equal. Thus, we have arrived at an absurd or impossible result. What is the cause of this absurdity or impossibility?

The reasoning in the proof is impeccable. How can correct reasoning result in an impossible (and therefore false) conclusion? Elementary logic tells us that one of the premises in the reasoning process must be false. But the only premise which can possibly be false is the original one, that AB is greater than AC. All the other premises are true, *if* it is true. (These premises are either based on the premise that AB is greater than AC or they are drawn from earlier proved propositions, such as Propositions 3 and 4.) It must therefore be the case that the initial assumption—that AB is greater than AC

—is false. Since we can similarly prove that it is false to say that AC is greater than AB, it must follow that AB is equal to AC. And this is the conclusion we were required to prove.

The foregoing illustrates the general procedure of proof by reduction to the absurd. Assume the contradictory of what is to be proved. Then, if by correct reasoning from that assumed premise, we arrive at a falsehood, we know that it must be due to the falsehood of that premise. And if that premise is false, then its contradictory must be true.

Reduction to the absurd is a very powerful tool. As we have indicated, Euclid uses it often in Book I, and he continues to use it throughout the *Elements*. Actually, if you investigate the various proofs that employ this method, you will find slight variations in them. One thing that makes reduction to the absurd so useful is the fact that it is not restricted to geometry; it works equally well in other fields.

IV

What is the role of the diagrams in Euclid's proofs?

In discussing the superposition proofs we mentioned that their dependence on geometrical intuition might constitute a possible objection to them. If there is any value whatever in that objection, it leads us to ask why there should be diagrams in any of the Euclidean proofs. Any diagram is, of course, an aid to intuition. Undoubtedly, the Euclidean diagrams are often helpful to us in following the proof. However, we cannot avoid asking whether the diagrams must be present in the proofs or whether they are only a convenience. Perhaps, we should even ask whether the presence of diagrams is legitimate, or whether they detract from the mathematical rigor of the proof.

The case for the diagrams is rather easily made. Geometry is about figures. Figures can be drawn and seen. Hence a geometrical proof should begin with a diagram. It shows us the very thing being talked about.

The objection to this would run as follows. Geometry is a branch of mathematics. Mathematics is a branch of, or extension of, logic. Nothing is needed for a mathematical proof except the definitions, postulates, axioms, and laws of logic. Arithmetic and algebra, for instance, do not use any diagrams. Therefore, the use of diagrams in geometry is superfluous and non-mathematical.

The pro-diagram side might say something like the following in rebuttal. Geometry is not arithmetic; hence not everything need be the same in these branches of mathematics. When you are talking about figures, why should it be wrong to exhibit the figures being talked about?

Here it would be countered that the presence of the drawn figures may mislead the reader into thinking that the proof is about these figures. We know, however, that the dots and lines on paper are not truly geometrical figures; that is, the points have parts and the lines have widths, unlike Euclid's points and lines. We know that the true geometrical objects are incapable of being physically drawn or visually seen.

The advocates of diagrams can point out that the physical properties of diagrams, such as the width of the lines, are never used in the proofs. Instead, Euclid uses only those properties of points, lines, and figures, which are either stated in the definitions and postulates, or else have already been proved by him. There is no attempt to say that the drawn triangle is the triangle which Euclid is talking about, but merely that it represents Euclid's triangle.

This gives rise to another objection. Drawn visible figures can never represent true geometrical figures. The particular properties of the diagram prevent it from representing the non-physical ideal geometrical figure. Thus, the proposition that the angles of a triangle are equal to two right angles is supposed to be true of all triangles. Yet the diagram drawn to accompany Proposition 32 shows an acute-angled triangle. Is the proposition also true of obtuse-angled triangles? If it is (and, of course, it is), then to use an acute-angled triangle in the diagram is a misrepresentation. Yet it has to be a misrepresentation, because no drawn triangle can be both acute-angled and obtuse-angled.

Here the answer is that although the triangle drawn has to

be acute-angled, or obtuse-angled, or right-angled, still the proof of the proposition in no way depends on the triangle's being any one of the three. In fact, not only this property, but all particularities of the drawn figure are ignored—that it is on this page, that it is drawn with red pencil, that its apex points south, and what not. No use is made of any particular attributes, and so the proof, and the proposition, is valid for all triangles.

We leave it to the reader to supply further steps in this exchange.

Does the way in which Euclid presents his propositions indicate the way in which they were discovered?

It should be obvious that the answer to this question is negative. There is no reason to think that Proposition 1 of the *Elements* was discovered before all others. We have already pointed out that many of the propositions in Euclid's *Elements* were not discovered by Euclid at all. Euclid's talent lies in presenting these propositions in the best way from the point of view of proof. This means that every step in a proof is warranted either by earlier proposition or by a postulate, that there are as few steps as possible, and that the proof is elegant.

The same considerations govern the arrangement of the entire book. Here, too, the way in which the series of 48 propositions is arranged is not indicative of the order in which they were discovered. The order is dictated by Euclid's desire that the book proceed from the simple to the complex, in as few steps as possible. It may well be that the famous Proposition 47 was discovered long before some of the intricate propositions that precede it, such as Proposition 45.

Does Euclid tell us how to measure the size of a triangle?

In Proposition 41, Euclid tells us that a triangle is half the size of a parallelogram which has the same base and is within the same parallels as the triangle. Since a rectangle is a special kind of parallelogram, we may also infer that a triangle is half the size of the rectangle having the same base with it and which is within the same parallels. This proposition gives us the area of the triangle, provided we know the area of the rectangle in question. Does Euclid, in Book I, tell us what the area of the rectangle is? Why do you suppose that he does not, but rather reserves the topic for Book VI, after he has developed the theory of ratios and proportions?

Why does Euclid not simply say, as we learn in high school, that "the area of a triangle is equal to one-half of the base times the altitude"? Is there any measurement in Book I of Euclid's *Elements?*

The following questions are designed to help you test the thoroughness of your reading. Each question is to be answered by giving a page or pages of the reading assignment. Answers will be found on page 223 of this Reading Plan.

1 In what propositions of Book I is the construction of a line parallel to a given line required?

2 The term "parallelogram" (or "parallelogrammic area") is not defined in the "Definitions." What proposition indicates what the definition is?

3 What is the "complement" of a parallelogram?

4 Common Notion 1 describes a property of equality which is called "transitivity." Is transitivity also a property of the relation of parallelism?

5 The adjoining diagram could be used to prove what proposition?

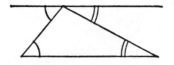

6 What is the contrary of Proposition 29?

ARCHIMEDES

On the Equilibrium of Planes

Book I

Prop. 1–7

Vol. 11, pp. 502–504

The names of many ancient mathematicians and scientists are quite unfamiliar to most of us. But there is one shining exception—Archimedes of Syracuse. His name usually calls to mind a man sitting in a bathtub with the water running over, then running out into the streets unclad, crying "Eureka (I have found it)," the "it" being the answer to a scientific problem. We like to think of him as typical of the man of science who is so immersed in his studies that he pays no attention to his surroundings. We also remember Archimedes' famous boast: "Give me a fulcrum (a place to rest a lever on), and I will move the earth."

Such boasting, legendary or not, was based on solid scientific knowledge of physical relations, in this case about weights and balances. We are inclined to think that, although the Greeks may have had keen mathematical insight, they entirely lacked knowledge of the structure of the physical world. We regard the science of physics as a modern development, dating back only to the 16th century.

A cursory glance at Archimedes' work on the equilibrium and centers of gravity of bodies should dispel this erroneous idea. Here is a work on theoretical physics, written in the 3rd century B.C. It deals with typical physical problems of weights, balances, and distances, and it demonstrates the solutions in much the same way as we do nowadays. The pages selected from this work will give you a vivid impression of the power and rigor of the Greek scientific mind.

Third Reading

I

With this reading assignment we pass from the realm of pure mathematics to another subject. It is difficult, however, to say precisely what this subject is. The book we are reading is written in mathematical form. It begins with seven postulates. These are followed by 15 propositions. Nevertheless, the things talked about—weights, distances, centers of gravity—make it abundantly clear that this is not a purely mathematical treatise, as is Euclid's *Elements*. Yet it is also quite clear that this is not an introduction to experimental natural science. In fact, it contains no record of experiments performed by Archimedes.

Certain natural phenomena, such as weight and equilibrium, are discussed. This seems to justify our saying that Archimedes is dealing with a branch of physics or natural science. This particular branch is usually called *statics*, since it deals with forces exerted by bodies at rest; by contrast, *dynamics* deals with bodies in motion and the forces involved. Furthermore, since mathematical analysis and proof are indispensable to Archimedes, it can also be said that the *Equilibrium of Planes* is an example of mathematical physics. It is probably the earliest such treatise.

II

How can a book about physics—even mathematical physics—get along without any experiments? How can what it says have any relevance to nature and natural phenomena, unless there is some experimentation which verifies the mathematical formulations, or else casts doubt on them?

The answer is that although there are no experiments reported in this work, it is nevertheless based on experience and observation. Of the seven postulates, the first three state conclusions that can only be known either by general observation or by special experimentation. How, except by looking, can Archimedes know that equal weights at equal distances from a fulcrum are in equilibrium? Again, is it not a matter of observation that when a weight is added to one side of a balance that is in equilibrium, then the equilibrium will be disturbed, the balance sinking on the side where the weight has been added?

In other words, the postulates in this work (or at least the first three postulates) constitute Archimedes' reservoir of what he and we know concerning the behavior of weights and balances. This knowledge is of a rather simple kind and probably was acquired not by elaborate or special experiments, but from common experience.

It is interesting to note the differences as well as the similarities between Euclid's postulates and Archimedes'. Both sets of postulates are undemonstrable. Yet they are vitally necessary to the treatise following them. Archimedes' postulates, being non-mathematical (we are here concerned with only the first three of them) are not constructional, as are the first three of Euclid's. The Archimedean postulates assert something about an experimental situation. Just as the Euclidean constructional postulates are followed by construction problems which are solved by showing that other constructions are possible, so Archimedes' postulates *could* be followed by experiments or observations. As a matter of fact, such additional experiments and observations are missing from this book. Hence this work corresponds to a mathematical treatise which contains no construction proofs.

The purpose of the first part of this book (through Proposition 7) may be described as follows. Everyone's experience testifies to certain facts about weights and levers. This common knowledge is recorded in the first three postulates. But this is knowledge of a general and imprecise kind; it involves no mathematically exact formulations. Archimedes' work transforms this general and imprecise knowledge into precisely formulated mathematical laws.

The foregoing indicates why no further experiments or observations are necessary. The *Equilibrium of Planes* takes existing experimental and observational knowledge and, with the help of mathematical tools, refines it and recasts it in different language. This is achieved in Propositions 6 and 7.

III

We must now take a closer look at Propositions 6 and 7. What comes before is preparatory to them; what follows them is in the nature of an anticlimax. Propositions 6 and 7 together constitute the so-called Law of the Lever.

Propositions 1-3 are all proved directly from the postulates. They are not very different from the postulates, nor perhaps any less obvious. But since they can be proved, there was no need for Archimedes to assume them. The first three postulates and the first three propositions can be summed up as follows:

A. Equal weights balance at equal distances; equal weights do not balance at unequal distances, but incline toward the weight at the greater distance. (Postulate 1 and Proposition 1)

B. Unequal weights do not balance at equal distances, but balance at unequal distances, the greater weight being at the lesser distance. (Propositions 2 and 3)

C. If equilibrium exists, it will be disturbed by weight being taken away from one side or added to one side. The balance will incline toward the side from which nothing is taken or to which something is added. (Postulates 2 and 3)

Propositions 4 and 5 make certain obvious statements about the center of gravity (that is, point of balance) of a system of equal weights, arrayed in a straight line. If there is an odd number of equal weights, then the center of gravity of the system coincides with the center of gravity of the middle weight. If there is an even number of equal weights, then the center of gravity of the system will be the mid-point between the two middle weights. These propositions are needed for the proof of the next two propositions.

Propositions 6 and 7 prove that unequal weights balance at

distances inversely proportional to the weights. Proposition 6 considers the case where the two weights are commensurable; that is, have some common measure. Proposition 7 deals with the case of two weights that have no common measure and are, therefore, incommensurable with one another.

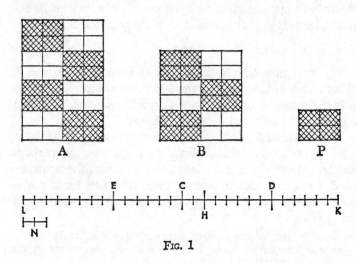

Fig. 1

To show how Archimedes proves Proposition 6, let us give actual numerical values to the weights and distances involved and follow his proof. Let weight A be 32 units (it does not matter whether the units be ounces, pounds, grams, or anything else). Let weight B be 24 of the same units. Then A and B are commensurable, for 32 and 24 are commensurable. Let DE be a straight line divided at C so that A:B :: DC:CE. For example, let DC be 8 units of length, and CE 6 units of length. Thus 32:24 :: 8:6.

8 and 6 are also commensurable; a common measure is 2. Now draw a straight line N = 2. Make DH and DK each equal to CE, that is, equal to 6. Make EL equal to CD or 8. Then E bisects LH, and D bisects HK.

LH = 16 and contains N, 8 times; HK = 12 and contains N, 6 times. Next, take a magnitude P, so that A contains P as many times as LH contains N. Since LH = 8N, this means that $A = 8P$. P therefore equals 4. Consequently B contains P, 6 times; that is, $B = 6P$. Therefore P is contained as many times (6) in B as N is contained in HK.

Now divide HK into its 6 parts equal to N, and divide LH into its 8 parts equal to N. Then divide A into its 8 parts equal to P, and then divide B into its 6 parts equal to P. Take each of the P's in A and place one at each of the middle points of the N's of LH. Similarly take each of the P's in B and place one at each of the middle points of the N's in HK.

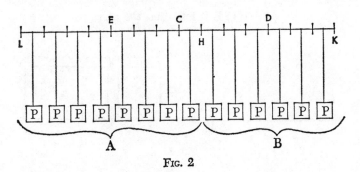

FIG. 2

Then the system of 8 P's which are equal to A balances about point E; and the system of 6 P's which are equal to B balances about D. Hence, Archimedes says, this situation is no different from what would obtain if A were itself applied at E, and B were applied at D. But the entire system of 14 P's balances about the point C, because there are 7 P's to the left of it and 7 P's to the right of it. Therefore A and B would also balance about the point C. This proves the proposition, for we already know that A:B :: DC:CE.

In the next section of this guide we will raise some questions concerning the validity of this proof. Right now, let us turn to the proof of the same law when A and B are incommensurable magnitudes (Proposition 7).

The proof is a reduction to the absurd, making use of the proposition just proved. Let A and B be incommensurable weights, and let DE be a line divided at C so that

$$A : B :: DC : CE.$$

Then it must be proved that A and B balance about point C. Let us assume, therefore, that they do *not* balance—that A is too large to balance B.

Now the trick of the proof consists in subtracting something from A which is *not* enough to make the remainder balance B, but which does make the remainder commensurable with B. Let the subtracted part be called q. Then since

$$A : B :: DE : CE$$

it follows that

$$(A - q) : B \text{ is less than } DC : CE.$$

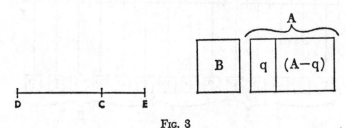

Fig. 3

Since A − q and B are commensurable, we know, by Proposition 6, that they would balance at distances reciprocally proportional to their weights; hence they do not balance at D and E. Instead, A − q is too small to balance B, at the given distances, and so the balance will be depressed at D.

But, by assumption, the amount q was too small to make the remainder A − q balance B, and so the balance will be depressed at E. But it is obviously impossible for the balance to be depressed both at D and at E. Hence the assumption that A and B do not balance at D and E is false, and its contradictory is true; namely, that they *do* balance.

IV

What are the assumptions underlying Archimedes' proof of Proposition 6?

The main assumption has to do with a double function of the center of gravity. No definition of the center of gravity is given by Archimedes, so we must try to detect the meaning of the term from the contexts in which it is used. It appears that two different meanings are used by Archimedes.

The first meaning, used in Propositions 4 and 5, is apparently that of a point of balance, or the point at which a fulcrum should be located in order to balance a system of weights. In this usage of the term, it makes good sense to say that the center of gravity of an uneven number of equal weights arrayed in a straight line should coincide with the center of gravity of the middle one.

The second meaning of center of gravity is a point at which we imagine the entire weight of a body or system of bodies concentrated and which is so located that the balance of the weight or system of weights is undisturbed whether the weight or weights are in their actual places or are imagined to be concentrated all at this one point.

This second meaning of the term "center of gravity" is the one used in Proposition 6. It is in virtue of this second meaning that we speak of a weight A acting at the point M of a balance. "Acting at the point M" here means, of course, exerting downward pull. According to the second meaning of center of gravity, this is a legitimate way of speaking. However, it must be realized that downward pull is being exerted not only at M, but also at all other points of the weight A, such as points X and Y. But if M is the center of gravity, then we may imagine all the downward pull as concentrated at that one point.

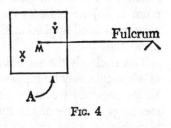

Fig. 4

The first of the two meanings of center of gravity seems easier to accept. Two major questions must be asked about the second meaning. First, is the notion of a point at which all the weight of a body is concentrated acceptable? (Here it is well to remember Euclid's definition of a point—that which has no parts.) Secondly, if we find this meaning acceptable, are the first and second meanings the same, or at least equivalent? If they are not, then at a minimum Archimedes is guilty of causing considerable confusion by using the same word with two different meanings.

More is at stake than mere equivocation, however, for in Proposition 6 it is absolutely necessary for Archimedes' proof that both meanings be the same. The point defined as center of gravity in the first sense must also be the center of gravity in the second sense.

The major device that Archimedes uses in his proof, it will be remembered, is to divide the original weights into a number of small weights and string them along the balance. In our restatement of the proof, eight equal parts (together equal to A) are set out at equal distances from one another along line LH. (See Fig. 2 on p. 39 of this guide.) Then, Archimedes says, the center of gravity of the eight weights will be at E, the mid-point of LH. Here E is the center of gravity in the first sense; that is, if LH were a balance and a fulcrum were placed at E, then the four weights to the left of E would balance the four weights to the right of E. However, it is important to realize that LH is not a balance and that there is no fulcrum at E. (The original line DE was a balance with a fulcrum at C.) Archimedes then goes on to say "Thus we may suppose A itself applied at E, and B itself applied at D." (See p. 504a.)

This is clearly the second meaning of center of gravity. All of A's weight may be supposed to be concentrated at the point E. But how do we know that this identification of the two meanings of center of gravity is legitimate? It no doubt seems plausible to make this identification, but plausibility is far from proof. Furthermore, there is even something dubious about calling E a center of gravity in the first sense, since E is not a fulcrum at all.

Do any of the foregoing considerations invalidate the proof? Could there be another proof of the proposition? What value would there be in experiments which tend to verify this proof?

Why must there be two proofs of the Law of the Lever, one for commensurable and one for incommensurable magnitudes?

To answer this question, we must first clearly understand what incommensurable magnitudes are. As the words indicate, magnitudes are incommensurable if they have no common measure. Thus, the numbers 24 and 36 are commensurable, since they have the number 4 as common measure. In fact, all whole numbers are commensurable with one another, since they all have at least the number one as common measure. Indeed, it is easy to see that a major question about incommensurable magnitudes is whether there actually are any. Not only are all whole numbers commensurable, but all ordinary fractions, like ½ or ¼, are also commensurable with one another and with whole numbers. (It was for this reason that we did not give any numerical version of the proof for Proposition 7.) The discovery that there really are incommensurable magnitudes is attributed to the Pythagoreans and is rightly considered quite a feat.

To say that there are two magnitudes which are incommensurable with one another means that there is no magnitude, *no matter how small,* which goes into both of them a whole number of times. If a small magnitude measures (goes into) one of them, then it will not measure the other one, and vice versa. The Pythagorean discovery probably was made in connection with Proposition 47 in Book I of Euclid's *Elements.* This proposition may have led someone to see that the side and diagonal of a square are incommensurable. In modern notation, this is expressed by saying that the number 1 (the side of the square) is incommensurable with the square root of 2 (the diagonal of the square).

Archimedes' proof of Proposition 6 depends on finding a common measure of the weights A and B and dividing each of them into parts equal to the common measure. These equal parts are then strung out along the line LK. It is obvious that this method of proof will not work for incommensurable magnitudes, since by definition they have no common measure. The proof—the reduction to the absurd—which Archimedes employs depends on another important property of magnitudes. That property is their infinite divisibility, or their capacity for being divided into parts no matter how small. The initial assumption of the proof (the assumption which must be shown to lead to an absurdity) is that A is too large to balance B. However, nothing is said about how much too large A is. It may, therefore, be a very small amount. Archimedes must be able to show that the assumption that A is too large to balance B leads to an absurdity, no matter how small A's excess is. And so he must be able to subtract from A an amount which makes the remainder commensurable with B and yet not large enough to balance B, even if the excess of A over the balancing amount is very small. *No matter how small* the excess is, Archimedes can always subtract from A a smaller amount that will make the remainder commensurable with B. This important property of infinite divisibility (without which Archimedes' proof would fail) is a property of continuous magnitudes. Whole numbers, for instance, do not possess it.

What is the Law of the Lever for magnitudes that do not balance?

The question can be elucidated as follows. Suppose we have two weights, and two distances from a fulcrum. Suppose, furthermore, that the distances are *not* reciprocally proportional to the weights. Then we know that the weights do not balance. But can we tell which side of the balance will be depressed?

Archimedes, in fact, seems to have this knowledge. For in the course of the proof of Proposition 7, he comes to this result:

A : B is less than DC : CE.

He concludes from this that D (the point at which B is applied) will be depressed. How does he reach this conclusion?

In modern terminology, this is done through the concept of a "moment of force." The moment consists of the product of the weight and the distance from the fulcrum at which that weight is applied. For balancing weights, the law of the lever is that the moments must be equal. And for non-balancing weights, the law is that the side with the smaller moment will rise, while the side with the larger moment will be depressed.

In our numerical example (see p. 38 of this guide), we assigned such values to the weights and distances that we had

$$32 : 24 :: 8 : 6.$$

And indeed, $32 \times 6 = 192$, and $24 \times 8 = 192$. Hence the moments are equal.

Now suppose that the two weights are 20 and 15 and that the bigger weight acts at the distance 8, while the lesser weight acts at the distance 10. Then the two moments are 20×8 or 160, and 15×10 or 150. Since 160 is greater than 150, the side with that moment, that is, the side with the weight 20, will be depressed.

The following questions are designed to help you test the thoroughness of your reading. Each question is to be answered by giving a page or pages of the reading assignment. Answers will be found on page 223 of this Reading Plan.

1 Will the following system be in equilibrium? There are four weights whose magnitudes are 10, 8, 8, 10. Their distances from the fulcrum (given in the same order as the weights) are 20 and 6 to the left of the fulcrum; and 6 and 20 to the right of the fulcrum.

2 Will the following system be in equilibrium? A weight of 30 units at a distance 2 from the fulcrum, and a weight of 10 units at a distance 6 from the fulcrum.

3 The center of gravity of a certain square made of uniform material is at the intersection of the diagonals. Will the center of gravity of all other squares of uniform material be also at the intersection of the diagonal?

4 Where, approximately, is the center of gravity of a uniform semisphere?

5 Two weights of size 12 and size 6 are at the distances 4 and 10 from the fulcrum, respectively. What must be done to get the system into equilibrium?

6 Two triangles are congruent. Will their centers of gravity also coincide?

46

NICOMACHUS

Introduction to Arithmetic

Book I, Ch. 1–16

Vol. 11, pp. 811–821

So far we have read texts which fit in with our contemporary notions of physics and mathematics. But the Greek scientific mind was not merely an early form of the modern. Mathematics to the Greeks was not only a useful method of calculating quantitative relations. It was also a divine science, almost a religion, having to do with eternal things. It was the way to wisdom, to knowledge of the eternal patterns in and behind all things.

This view of mathematics was most prominent in the teachings of Pythagoras and his followers. Nicomachus of Gerasa, the author of the *Introduction to Arithmetic*, was a member of this school. In the *Introduction*, the talk is all about numbers, and what talk it is, indeed! Numbers here have to do with the eternal harmonies, the music of the spheres. Numbers are not only signs of the eternal patterns, but they possess definite characteristics. They are not only even or odd, but perfect

47

or imperfect, friendly or unfriendly, prime or not prime. Arithmetic is not merely a matter of detached, unimpassioned calculation, but an aesthetic, even a religious, search.

Scientists today, with notable exceptions, are not inclined to attribute any moral qualities to numbers or to numerical relations. But increasingly they seek for a numerical formulation of the facts and structure of the physical world. Somewhat like Nicomachus, they believe that numbers are the signs of the underlying patterns in nature. Greek and modern alike seem to echo Solomon's sentiment, who, speaking to the Lord, said: "Thou hast ordered all things in measure, and number, and weight."

I

This is an elementary work in arithmetic; but it is altogether different in approach and style from Euclid's elementary work in geometry. Whereas Euclid's *Elements* can, and sometimes does, serve even today as a textbook for the study of geometrical theorems, it is not likely that Nicomachus' work would be deemed useful in today's classrooms. Few students and teachers today would recognize it as a book dealing with arithmetic, at least not as we understand that subject.

What is the difference between these two works which accounts for the fact that one has remained meaningful to us moderns, while the other one strikes us as archaic? Both are works in mathematics, and we may safely say that the truths of mathematics are timeless—arithmetical truths as well as geometrical ones. Indeed, it is not the case that what Nicomachus has to tell us is no longer true. But the problems which he treats are now generally neglected.

Nicomachus spends no time on what we might expect to find in a book about arithmetic. He gives us no rules for the addition and subtraction of numbers. He tells us nothing about the processes of multiplication and division. We do not learn about operating with fractions, let alone such recondite things as roots, powers, and exponents. In a word, Nicomachus is not at all interested in arithmetical operations. Instead, his concern is with numbers as such, and with their properties, their relations and their classification. Hence the book might fairly be called an "Introduction to Numbers" or "Number Theory."

Nicomachus' aims and methods indicate that he belongs to the school of Pythagoras—that group of mathematicians and philosophers whom we have already mentioned several times in this Reading Plan. The Pythagoreans were not content simply to study mathematics, but, as Aristotle tells us, "they thought its principles were the principles of all things." (See Vol. 8, p. 503d.) Aristotle continues his description of the Pythagorean view as follows:

Since of these principles numbers are by nature the first, and in numbers they seemed to see many resemblances to the things that exist and come into being—more than in fire and earth and water (such and such a modification of numbers being justice, another being soul and reason, another being opportunity—and similarly almost all other things being numerically expressible); since, again, they saw that the modifications and the ratios of the musical scales were expressible in numbers;—since, then, all other things seemed in their whole nature to be modelled on numbers, and numbers seemed to be the first things in the whole of nature, they supposed the elements of numbers to be the elements of all things, and the whole heaven to be a musical scale and a number. And all the properties of numbers and scales which they could show to agree with the attributes and parts and the whole arrangement of the heavens, they collected and fitted into their scheme; and if there was a gap anywhere, they readily made additions so as to make their whole theory coherent. (*Metaphysics*, Bk. I, Ch. 5, Vol. 8, pp. 503d-504a)

According to this explanation, the study of numbers is part of cosmology for the Pythagoreans. In learning about the properties of numbers, we learn about the properties of the elementary constituent parts of things. Nicomachus, writing around A.D. 100, confirms Aristotle's report on the Pythagorean school, which was written in 350 B.C.

The aim of human life, Nicomachus points out, is the acquisition of wisdom; indeed, philosophy means the "love of wisdom." But wisdom, according to Pythagoras, is "the knowledge, or science, of the truth in real things" (p. 811a-b). Now what are these real things? They cannot be bodily, material things, for these are "forever involved in continuous flow and change." By contrast certain "bodiless things . . . are of themselves immovable and unchangeable," namely, such things as

. . . qualities, quantities, configurations, largeness, smallness, equality, relations, actualities, dispositions, places, times . . . (p. 811b)

Wisdom, then, consists in the study of these "accidents." The term "accident" comes from Aristotle's *Categories*, where nine kinds of accidental attributes of things are enumerated: quantity, quality, relation, place, time, position, state, action, affection. (See Vol. 8, p. 5d.) Aristotle's and Nicomachus' enumerations, it will be noted, are similar but not the same.

In opening his study of the accidental but unchanging attributes of things, Nicomachus begins by noting that of all things

> . . . some of them [are] unified and continuous . . . which are properly and peculiarly called "magnitudes"; others are discontinuous, in a side-by-side arrangement, and, as it were, in heaps, which are called "multitudes . . ." (pp. 811d-812a)

Magnitude and multitude, however, are too indefinite to be subjects of study; instead, we must concern ourselves with size and quantity. "Wisdom, then," Nicomachus concludes, "must be considered to be the knowledge of these two forms." (p. 812a)

There are four mathematical sciences in the Pythagorean scheme. In addition to arithmetic and geometry (dealing, respectively, with quantity and size), there are two more sciences. One is music, which deals with quantity in its relative aspects; i.e., with ratios and proportions. The other is astronomy, which deals with size insofar as it moves; i.e., especially with the motions of circles.

We are accustomed to think of mathematics as divided into arithmetic and geometry. To have music and astronomy added to these two is surprising. It is especially important to bear in mind that Nicomachus means to consider them as true branches of pure mathematics, and not merely as sciences that apply mathematics. This probably sounds odd to the modern reader. We are not used to thinking of music as a science at all, but as an art; and we consider astronomy as a branch of physics or of applied mathematics. For the Pythagoreans, however, both music and astronomy are branches of pure mathematics. Nicomachus quotes with approval Socrates' words (from *The Republic*) to the effect that all the mathematical sciences—arithmetic, geometry, music, and astronomy—are to be studied for the sake of wisdom only, not for the sake of their utility. (See pp. 812d-813a.)

This disregard or even disdain for practical utility helps to explain the character and content of Nicomachus' work. It is not intended to teach us the rules of arithmetical operations. No more would a book on astronomy, written by a Pythagorean, be intended to teach us how to calculate eclipses or how to devise an accurate calendar. Such utilitarian tasks would be relegated to a practical manual, having the character of a cookbook.

Arithmetic and astronomy are studied for their own sake. The arithmetician is interested in finding out the truths about numbers, not in using numbers. The following paragraph sums up the attitude of the Pythagoreans and of Nicomachus with regard to numbers.

All that has by nature with systematic method been arranged in the universe seems both in part and as a whole to have been determined and ordered in accordance with number, by the forethought and the mind of him that created all things; for the pattern was fixed, like a preliminary sketch, by the domination of number preëxistent in the mind of the world-creating God, number conceptual only and immaterial in every way, but at the same time the true and the eternal essence, so that with reference to it, as to an artistic plan, should be created all these things, time, motion, the heavens, the stars, all sorts of revolutions. (pp. 813d-814a)

II

An example of the Pythagorean way of treating numbers is given by the division of numbers into even and odd, and further, into even-times even, even-times odd, odd-times even, and odd-times odd. Most of us are familiar with the fact that numbers can be divided into even and odd, but the other divisions have an unfamiliar ring. Furthermore, it is probably accurate to say that the distinction between even and odd strikes most of us as simple and unimportant. Numbers, in the modern view, are all of one kind; there is no point in dwelling on such a minor difference as that between even and odd.

To Nicomachus, however, numbers are not pale, shadowy things that are all alike. Each number is for him a very important and real thing. One reason why numbers have such reality for Nicomachus is that he considers only the natural numbers, the positive whole numbers. He does not give the name of number to such things as fractions, negative numbers, surds, or imaginary numbers. These are excluded from the realm of numbers, and so are the operations which give rise to them. Thus Nicomachus does not admit the possibility of arriving at a numerical result, if it is proposed to divide 8 into 5, or to subtract 12 from 7, or to extract the square root of 10.

Each number is, in Nichomachus' view, different from every other one; each number has its distinct properties and qualities. Numbers can be classified according to these qualities. We are called upon to determine what these classifications are and to which classes a number belongs, just as the moralist is expected to classify men according to whether they have good or bad characters. As a matter of fact, Nicomachus probably would not hesitate to speak of the "character" of numbers and to apply the appellations "good" and "bad" to them. We know that he speaks of "perfect" numbers and that the Pythagoreans had the concepts of "friendly" numbers. (Both perfect and friendly numbers will be discussed presently.)

It is interesting to compare Nicomachus' classification of numbers into even-times even, even-times odd, odd-times even, and odd-times odd (though he does not mention the last category by name) with Euclid's classification. Though there is much in Euclid's work that is derived from other mathematicians and though a considerable portion of the contents of the *Elements* was, no doubt, contributed by the Pythagoreans, Euclid's work is not, as such, Pythagorean in character. He treats the subject of numbers, for instance, much more matter-of-factly than Nicomachus, without the latter's typically Pythagorean awe and mysticism. Euclid's classification of numbers, according to the principles of odd and even, is, therefore, less elaborate than Nicomachus' and, consequently, much more like what we would expect.

Euclid simply divides numbers into the following classes: the even-times even, which are numbers that are the product of two even numbers; the even-times odd, which are numbers that are the product of an even and an odd number; and the odd-times odd, which are numbers that are the product of two odd numbers. (See the *Elements*, Book VII, Definitions 8-10, in Vol. 11, p. 127a.) According to these definitions, a number may be both even-times even and even-times odd. Thus 12 would be both, since it is 2×6 as well as 3×4.

Nicomachus' more elaborate classification makes it impossible for a number to fall into more than one class. Thus, for him the number 12 is neither even-times even nor even-times odd, but odd-times even.

In the Nicomachean scheme, "even-times even" signifies numbers that have *only* even factors. In other words, these numbers are the powers of two. Examples of even-times even numbers are 4, 8, 16, 32, 64, . . . 2^n.

The even-times odd number, in Nicomachus' scheme as distinguished from Euclid's, is an even number that can, of course, be divided by 2, but the remaining factor is an odd number. An example is 6, which is 2×3, or 10, which is 2×5. But the number 12 is not even-times odd, for it is 2×6, and 6 is not an odd number.

However, 12 is an example of what Nicomachus calls an odd-times even number. These numbers can be divided by 2 several times (more than once), and thus they are not even-times odd. On the other hand, the divisions cannot be carried on indefinitely without arriving at an odd number. Hence these numbers are distinct from the even-times even numbers. 12, for instance, can be divided by 2, yielding 6, and 6 can be divided by 2 again, yielding 3. Since more than one division by 2 is possible, the number 12 is not even-times odd, and since the division ends by yielding an odd number, namely 3, the number 12 is not even-times even. This kind of number, therefore, is called odd-times even by Nichomachus. It is clear that the three kinds of even numbers constitute exclusive categories, and furthermore are exhaustive of all even numbers.

III

What is a perfect number?

The notion that perfection is predicable of numbers is a typically Pythagorean concept. Perfect numbers are, like all good things, few and far between. Euclid defines them thus: "A *perfect number* is that which is equal to its own parts." (See *Elements*, Book VII, Definition 22, in Vol. 11, p. 128a.) Nicomachus' definition, though somewhat more flowery, is the same as Euclid's. (See p. 820d.) The number 6 is perfect, because the sum of all its "parts" or factors is equal to 6. The factors of 6 are 1, 2, and 3, and of course $1 + 2 + 3 = 6$. In general, then, we take all the numbers by which a given number is divisible, including 1, and add them up. If they add up to the original number, that number is called *perfect*. If the sum of all the factors is greater than the original number, then that number is *superabundant;* and if the factors are less, the number is *deficient*.

For example, the number 8 is deficient. It is divisible by 1, 2, and 4. But $1 + 2 + 4 = 7$, which is less than 8. On the other hand, the number 12 is superabundant. For 12 is divisible by 1, 2, 3, 4, and 6. And $1 + 2 + 3 + 4 + 6 = 16$, which is more than 12.

Another perfect number is 28. For 28 is divisible by 1, 2, 4, 7, and 14. And $1 + 2 + 4 + 7 + 14 = 28$.

A method of finding perfect numbers is recorded in Euclid's *Elements*. As a matter of fact, Euclid probably considered it the climax of his work in arithmetic, since he shows us the method only in the last proposition of all those dealing with numbers (Book IX, Prop. 36, Vol. 11, p. 189a). The method is as follows. Consider, successively, all the powers of 2, i.e., 2^2, 2^3, 2^4, etc. Subtract 1 from each of these powers. If the resulting number is prime (not divisible except by 1), then multiply the resulting number by the previous power of 2.

Thus we have: $2^2 = 4$. $4 - 1 = 3$, which is prime. Therefore, multiply 3 by the previous power of 2, or $2^1 = 2$. And $3 \times 2 = 6$. Then 6 is a perfect number.

Next consider $2^3 = 8$. $8 - 1 = 7$, which is prime. Multiply 7 by 4, the previous power of 2 (i.e., 2^2). $7 \times 4 = 28$, which is perfect.

Next consider $2^4 = 16$. $16 - 1 = 15$, which is not prime.

Next consider $2^5 = 32$. $32 - 1 = 31$, which is prime. Multiply 31 by 16. $31 \times 16 = 496$, which is perfect.

Next consider $2^6 = 64$. $64 - 1 = 63$, which is not prime.

Next consider $2^7 = 128$. $128 - 1 = 127$, which is prime. Multiply 127 by 64. $127 \times 64 = 8,128$, which is perfect.

You can see that the perfect numbers are rare and are already beginning to be quite large. Nicomachus thought that there was just one perfect number in each "order." There is one in the units, namely 6. Another perfect number is in the tens, namely 28. In the hundreds there is 496, and in the thousands we have 8,128. That is all the perfect numbers Nicomachus knew; actually it turns out that there is no perfect number in the ten thousands. Indeed the next perfect number is in the order of the ten millions.

The difficulty in finding perfect numbers consists in determining whether $2^n - 1$ is a prime number or not. Once it is determined that the number is prime, we need only multiply. Some other perfect numbers are

$$(2^{13} - 1) \times 2^{12} = 33,550,336$$
$$(2^{17} - 1) \times 2^{16} = 8,589,869,056.$$

Several other numbers of the type $2^n - 1$ which are prime and which consequently make $(2^n - 1)(2^{n-1})$ perfect have been found. *Encyclopaedia Britannica* lists them in the article entitled, NUMBERS, THEORY OF.

Related to the perfect numbers are the "friendly" numbers. These are pairs of numbers so constituted that the sum of the factors of one number adds up to the second number. A pair of such friendly numbers is 220 and 284. The factors of 220 are 1, 2, 4, 5, 10, 11, 20, 22, 44, 55, 110. And $1 + 2 + 4 + 5 + 10 + 11 + 20 + 22 + 44 + 55 + 110 = 284$. The factors of 284 are 1, 2, 4, 71, 142; and $1 + 2 + 4 + 71 + 142 = 220$. Sir Thomas L. Heath, the translator of Euclid's and Archimedes' works in Volume 11, mentions the subject of perfect and friendly numbers in a work entitled *A History of Greek Mathematics* and remarks that the famous 18th-century mathematician Euler discovered 61 pairs of friendly numbers.

What is a prime number?

Nicomachus describes prime numbers as a kind of odd number. Having divided even numbers into three kinds (even-even, even-odd, odd-even), he similarly divides odd numbers into three kinds, namely, prime, composite, and relatively prime. Composite numbers are odd numbers that can be divided by other odd numbers. Examples are 39 (divisible by 3 and 13) and 35 (divisible by 5 and 7). Two numbers are relatively prime to each other if they have no common factor, although each of the two numbers is composite. Thus 9 and 35 are relatively prime, since $9 = 3 \times 3$ and $35 = 5 \times 7$.

Prime numbers are numbers that are not divisible except by 1 (and by themselves). Examples of prime numbers are 3, 5, 7, 11, 13. According to Nicomachus' classification, 2 is not a prime number, since it is even. However, it is true of 2 that it has no factors save 1 and itself, and so it is usually considered as prime and, incidentally, as the only even prime number.

Euclid deals with prime numbers at length. Proposition 20 of Book IX (see pp. 183d-184a) is a very important theorem concerning prime numbers. If you run over the prime numbers between, say, 1 and 100, you will notice that the gaps between them become greater and greater; in other words, the prime numbers decrease in frequency. Nevertheless, Euclid tells us in Book IX, Proposition 20, that the number of prime numbers is greater than any given number, or, in others words, that there are infinitely many prime numbers. This theorem may appear paradoxical at first. Although the prime numbers become rarer, they are still infinite in number, that is, there are as many primes as there are even numbers, or odd numbers, or, indeed, whole numbers.

Euclid's proof is a masterpiece of simplicity and beauty and requires no presuppositions. Here, with slight rephrasing, is the gist of it. The method is that of reduction to the absurd. Euclid assumes the opposite of what is to be proved, namely that the number of prime numbers is not greater than any given number. He assumes, in other words, that the number of prime numbers is equal to a given finite number. In that case, he continues, there must be a greatest prime number. Now multiply all the prime numbers up to the greatest one. Calling the supposedly greatest prime number P, this means that we must form the product $2 \times 3 \times 5 \times 7 \times 11 \times 13 \times 17 \times 19 \times 23 \times \ldots$ P. Add 1 to this product and call the result S.

Now concerning this new number S, the product of all the

prime numbers up to P plus 1, there are two possibilities. Either it is a prime number, or it is a composite number. If S *is* a prime number, then our proposition has been proved; for S is prime and is larger than P. But the assumption was that P is the largest prime number. And so that assumption has been proved absurd.

If, however, this number S is not prime, then it must have prime numbers as factors (since that is what it means for a number not to be prime). Now, none of these factors can be any of the prime numbers up to P, for if S is divided by any of them it must leave a remainder of 1 [since the number S is $(2 \times 3 \times 5 \times 7 \times \ldots \times P) + 1$]. Hence, any prime factor F that S has must be greater than P. And so we have in any case a greater prime number than P (either S itself, or F). Since this contradicts the assumption that P is the largest prime number, that assumption is false, and so we have shown that there is no prime number that is largest.

For example, if it were claimed that there are only three prime numbers, 2, 3, and 5, we would form the product of $2 \times 3 \times 5$ which is 30, and add 1 to it. This gives us 31. Now 31 is a prime number, and so it is disproved that there are only three prime numbers. With the addition of 31 there are at least four prime numbers. (As a matter of fact, there are several other prime numbers between 5 and 31.)

Again, suppose that it is claimed that there are only six prime numbers, viz., 2, 3, 5, 7, 11, 13. Then we form the product of $2 \times 3 \times 5 \times 7 \times 11 \times 13$. This gives us 30,030. We add 1 to it and get 30,031. Now this is not itself a prime number, but it has two prime factors, each of them greater than 13, viz., 59 and 509. Hence there are at least eight prime numbers; and this disproves the assumption that there are only six prime numbers.

Is the Pythagorean concern with numbers foolish and superstitious or is there some point to it?

We must be clear about the sense in which the Pythagoreans are concerned with numbers. Modern mathematicians are still concerned with numbers, and with such properties of them as primeness, evenness, perfectness, etc. All these properties are treated in the Theory of Numbers. It is unlikely that modern mathematicians would give to the properties of numbers such fancy names as "perfect," but aside from that minor difference, the theory of numbers has been studied by such famous mathematicians as Descartes, Fermat, Euler, Gauss, and many others.

Perhaps the Pythagoreans went to extremes when they made number a cosmological principle and considered numbers as the elements or principles of things. Nevertheless, there is a definite tendency toward a modified Pythagoreanism in modern science. For instance, modern science insists on trying to measure every actual phenomenon. Until a phenomenon has been measured and expressed in mathematical formulas, it is not considered to be thoroughly understood.

Does this mean that number is a cosmological principle in modern science? Or is there a difference between the way in which numbers function in 20th-century science and in Greek science? Does the fact that the Pythagoreans restricted themselves to natural numbers, while we employ fractions, negative numbers, irrationals, etc., make any difference to the role which numbers play in science?

The following questions are designed to help you test the thoroughness of your reading. Each question is to be answered by giving a page or pages of the reading assignment. Answers will be found on page 223 of this Reading Plan.

1 Why is arithmetic the most important of the mathematical sciences, in Nicomachus' view?

2 What kind of a number is 48?

3 Is the half of an even-times odd number even or odd?

4 How does Nicomachus define "number"?

5 What are numbers that are relatively prime?

6 What is the Pythagorean definition of "even"?

ARCHIMEDES

On Floating Bodies

Book I, Postulate 1

Prop. 1–7

Vol. 11, pp. 538–541

In this era of atomic power and space exploration, we tend to forget the more mundane physical situations and problems. With such complicated goings-on attracting the attention of our best scientific brains, we may be shy about asking such questions as "What makes a rubber ball bounce?" or "Why does a balloon go up?" But here is Archimedes, the great physical theorist of antiquity, answering the question "Why do bodies float in water?"

The old master does this in the course of a treatise on what we would now call Hydrostatics, but which he entitles more simply and concretely, "Floating Bodies." His discussion is a masterpiece of simplicity. All he asks us to grant him is a single postulate stating the characteristics of water and other fluids. The rest is simply a matter of geometrical reasoning. This is all

we need for the study of floating bodies, with Archimedes as our teacher.

The odd and wonderful thing about this is that you
do not even need water or objects to put in it. It may
be fun to verify some of the theoretical demonstrations
in the washbowl or bathtub. But Archimedes gives us
the scientific essentials about floating bodies without
experimentation. As you follow him along, you, too,
may want to cry out "Eureka."

I

This is our second reading from Archimedes' works. As *On the Equilibrium of Planes* was the first treatise dealing with the science of statics, so *On Floating Bodies* contains the foundations of hydrostatics. Again we see Archimedes' skill and inventiveness at work, as with a few assumptions he elegantly derives the most important theorems concerning bodies wholly or partially submerged in a liquid.

Archimedes was not only a first-rate scientist, but also a brilliant mathematician. Since this is our last reading from Archimedes' work, we will not have an opportunity to see his mathematical skill displayed. Let us, therefore, mention briefly some of his achievements in that field.

Archimedes' specialty lay in dealing with curved surfaces and lines. Whereas Euclid restricted himself to circles and straight lines, Archimedes found formulas for the surface and volume of a sphere and cone. He calculated the area of a segment of a parabola, and gave a numerical approximation to the circumference of a circle. (Incidentally, he arrived at a very good value for π, which is the ratio between the circumference and the diameter of a circle.) He devoted an entire book to a certain kind of spiral, named after him the "Archimedean spiral." Still another book deals with solids of revolution. These solids result when the conic sections (ellipses, parabolas, hyperbolas) are revolved about their axes. Finally, we must mention one of his most extraordinary mathematical achievements. In *The Sand-Reckoner*, Archimedes devises a notation for very large numbers. (We must remember that he did not have the decimal system available.) According

63

to Sir Thomas L. Heath, who translated his works, the largest number expressible in Archimedes' system would be written by us as 1 followed by 80,000 million millions of zeroes.

II

It is not surprising that a man of such great and varied skills as Archimedes should have been famous even among his contemporaries and that a great many fabulous stories concerning him have come down to us from antiquity. His mechanical inventions are said to have helped his native Syracuse defend herself when the Romans besieged her. Plutarch, in his life of Marcellus, devotes several pages to the accomplishments of Archimedes during this siege. (See Vol. 14, pp. 252a-255a.) It appears that Archimedes almost single-handedly held off the Romans by means of his machines, until the Romans "began to think they were fighting with the gods." (See Vol. 14, p. 253c.) The Roman general, Marcellus, bitterly complained about Archimedes' success:

"What," said he, "must we give up fighting with this geometrical Briareus, who plays pitch-and-toss with our ships, and, with the multitude of darts which he showers at a single moment upon us, really outdoes the hundred-handed giants of mythology?" And, doubtless, the rest of the Syracusans were but the body of Archimedes's designs, one soul moving and governing all; for, laying aside all other arms, with this alone they infested the Romans and protected themselves. In fine, when such terror had seized upon the Romans, that, if they did but see a little rope or a piece of wood from the wall, instantly crying out, that there it was again, Archimedes was about to let fly some engine at them, they turned their backs and fled, Marcellus desisted from conflicts and assaults, putting all his hope in a long siege. (Vol. 14, p. 253c-d)

Perhaps the best-known story about Archimedes relates to the so-called "crown problem." Hiero, the King of Syracuse, wished to know whether a crown, made of gold and silver, contained a greater admixture of silver than it was supposed to have. He asked Archimedes to determine the ratio of gold to silver in the crown, without, of course, melting down the crown. According to the traditional story, the solution came to Archimedes while he was in the bathtub. He was so overjoyed at his discovery that he jumped out of the tub, and ran naked through the streets of Syracuse, shouting "Eureka, eureka!" (meaning, "I have found it!"). The solution of the crown problem depends on the theory developed in *On Floating Bodies,* and we shall shortly see why it is appropriate that Archimedes' insight should have come to him while he was in the tub.

III

It is a simple fact of observation that some materials float in water and that others sink. Thus, for example, we all know that wood floats, while iron sinks. Put a board of wood in the water and it will stay on top; but if you put an iron plate, of the same size and shape as the wood, into the water, it will sink rapidly to the bottom. So much is easy. But how is it, then, that ships made of iron stay afloat? Archimedes solves this problem.

Even before going into the details of Archimedes' answer, we all realize that the shape of the ship has something to do with its buoyancy. Suppose the ship to consist only of the hull. If the amount of steel that goes into the hull were melted down again and recast in the shape of a solid cube, there is no doubt that this cube would sink.

What causes the iron ship to float when the steel is shaped like a hollow hull? The hull *displaces* water. Where the ship is, there the water is pushed away. The same thing happens if a person steps into a bathtub that was filled to the brim. Water is displaced in order to make room for the person. The evidence of this is the water's overflowing the tub. This was presumably what Archimedes observed when the solution to the crown problem flashed through his head. Similarly, when a ship is launched in the ocean, some water is displaced and the level of the ocean rises slightly. Of course, the disparity in volume between ship and ocean is so great that the rise in the ocean's level is unnoticeable; nevertheless, it is there.

The amount of water displaced is equal in volume to the volume of the body submerged in the water. This volume of water has a certain weight. Archimedes' discovery with respect to bodies in water or other fluids can be stated as follows: an upward force is exerted on such a body equal to the weight of the water displaced by the body. Hence, if the water which is displaced weighs more than the body in the water, the body will not sink but float in the water. Such a body will be partially submerged; and the submerged part will displace an amount of water equal in weight to the total weight of the body in the water. If the water which is displaced weighs less than the body in the water, the body will sink, but if it is weighed in the water it will be lighter than if weighed in air, by an amount equal to the weight of the displaced water.

The first four propositions of the work are preliminary. The cross-section of a sphere, through the center, is always a circle (Prop. 1). If a body equal in specific gravity with a certain fluid is submerged in that fluid, it will neither sink to the bottom nor stick out of the fluid, but will rest just below the surface (Prop. 3). A body lighter than the fluid in which it is submerged will partially submerge and partially project out of the fluid (Prop. 4).

Proposition 5 answers the question, "How far will such a light body be submerged?" Looking at the symmetry of the diagram that goes with Proposition 5 (see p. 540a), we can see that it must be submerged just so far that the amount of water displaced equals the weight of the body. In the diagram, the body EGHF must be balanced by the amount of water STUV, since elsewhere every part of the fluid on the left side is balanced by a corresponding part of the fluid on the right. STUV is equal in size to the submerged part of the body EGHF. If these two are to balance, STUV, or the water displaced by BGHC, must equal in weight the body EGHF.

Now what happens, Archimedes asks in Proposition 6, when a body lighter than water is forcibly pushed all the way into the water? An upward force is created, which tends to push the body back into its floating position. (Children know this when they forcibly submerge their floating toys in the bathtub; when they release the toy, it pops upwards, often even momentarily out of the water altogether.) Archimedes wants to know how large this upward force is.

The answer is easy. Let us look at the diagram for Proposition 5 rather than Proposition 6. If no downward force is exerted and equilibrium is permitted to establish itself, a portion of the body projects out of the fluid. This projecting portion is EBCF. If EBCF is forcibly immersed in the fluid, this can be accomplished only by displacing a volume of fluid equal to EBCF. The upward thrust which must be overcome to keep the entire body EGHF, including the portion EBCF, submerged is equal to the weight of the water displaced by EBCF.

Propositions 5 and 6 depend on the same principle. (And so, we shall see, does Proposition 7.) When a body is in water, an upward thrust is exerted on it equal to the weight of the amount of water displaced. Proposition 5 envisages the equilibrium situation, where upward thrust of displaced water and downward thrust of the submerged body are equalized. Proposition 6 envisages the case of an additional force being exerted to hold the body all the way under water. Since in that case more water is displaced, a greater upward thrust is generated and so there is no equilibrium.

Proposition 7 deals with a body heavier than water. It sinks to the bottom. However, it displaces a certain amount of water. This amount of water exerts an upward thrust equal to its weight. This upward thrust is not enough to make the submerged body float, since the body is too heavy. The thrust does, however, lighten the submerged body. In fact, if a submerged body is weighed while it is in the water, it is found to be lighter than in air.

IV

How might the "crown problem" have been solved?

We know that the crown contains only two metals, namely gold and silver. Furthermore the total weight of the crown is known, or easily ascertainable. The problem is to find how much gold is in the crown, and how much silver is in it.

No one knows, of course, how Archimedes solved the problem; nor, indeed, whether there really was such a problem or whether this is only a pleasant legend. But the following is one way in which the problem might have been solved.

Weigh the crown. Call its weight W. Next, place the crown in a container of water which is filled to the brim and fitted with a device to measure the amount of water that overflows if anything is added. In this way measure the amount of water displaced by the crown when placed in water. This volume of water is the same as the volume of the crown. Call this volume V.

Now take an amount of pure gold equal in weight to W. Measure its volume in the same way as the crown's volume was measured. Call this volume V_g.

Now take an amount of pure silver equal in weight to W. Measure its volume in the same way as the crown's volume and the volume of the pure gold. Call this volume V_s.

Now we are looking for two unknown weights, the weight of gold in the crown and the weight of silver in the crown. Call the first of these W_g, and the second one, W_s. Together, these two weights must equal the weight of the crown. That is, $W_g + W_s = W$.

What would be the volume of W_g, the unknown weight of gold in the crown? We know the volume of the weight W of gold, since we measured it and found it to be V_g. Hence we know that

$$\frac{\text{volume of } W_g}{V_g} = \frac{W_g}{W}$$

or

$$\text{volume of } W_g = \frac{W_g}{W} \times V_g$$

Similarly, for the volume of the unknown weight of silver W_s, we find

$$\text{volume of } W_s = \frac{W_s}{W} \times V_s$$

But the two volumes together must be equal to the volume of

the crown, just as the two weights together must be equal to the weight of the crown. That is,

$$\text{volume of } W_g + \text{volume of } W_s = V$$

or

$$\frac{W_g}{W} \times V_g + \frac{W_s}{W} \times V_s = V$$

or

$$
\begin{aligned}
W_g \times V_g + W_s \times V_s &= V \times W \\
&= V \times (W_g + W_s) \\
&= W_g \times V + W_s \times V
\end{aligned}
$$

And so

$$
\begin{aligned}
W_g \times V_g - W_g \times V &= W_s \times V - W_s \times V_s \\
W_g(V_g - V) &= W_s(V - V_s) \\
\frac{W_g}{W_s} &= \frac{V - V_s}{V_g - V}
\end{aligned}
$$

This is the required ratio. Since we know the total weight W of the crown, we can also find the exact weight of the gold and silver.

Let us illustrate the result with an example. Suppose that the original crown weighs 80 grams. Let it turn out that its volume, as measured by the displaced water, is 5 cubic centimeters. Then we have $W = 80$, $V = 5$.

Next, take 80 grams of pure gold and see how much water this displaces. Suppose that this is 4 cubic centimeters. Then we have $V_g = 4$.

Similarly, take 80 grams of pure silver and determine its volume. Suppose that this is 8 cubic centimeters. Then we have $V_s = 8$.

Now enter these values in our formula and find:

$$\frac{W_g}{W_s} = \frac{5 - 8}{4 - 5} = \frac{-3}{-1} = \frac{3}{1}$$

Thus there is three times as much gold in the crown as there is silver; in other words, there are 60 grams of gold and 20 grams of silver in it.

How would you measure the amount of weight a body loses by being immersed in water?

Throughout this guide we have spoken of the amount of weight a body loses when weighed in water (or some other fluid). How can we check this loss of weight experimentally? Suppose we weighed a body on a beam scale, in air, determining its weight by the number of grams it takes to balance it. Suppose, furthermore, that we immersed everything—body, scale, and weights—in water. Could we in this way find the weight loss suffered by the body?

A difficulty is obvious at once. Not only the body to be weighed, but also the graduated weights used as counterbalance lose weight in water. If the body being weighed and the counterbalancing weights have the same volume, then the scale will still be in balance in the water, for both the body to be weighed and the weights will lose an equal amount of weight. If one side has a greater volume than the other side, that side will sustain a greater loss of weight and consequently that side will rise when the balance is immersed in water.

One way of coping with this difficulty would be to employ a spring balance; i.e., a balance that measures weight not by a counterbalancing weight, but by the tension created in a spring. Such tension would be unaffected by submersion in water.

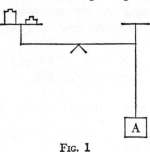

FIG. 1

Still another way would be to immerse the body to be weighed in water, while arranging the experimental conditions so that the counterbalanced weights are kept out of the water, as in the accompanying diagrams.

In Figure 1, the body A is weighed in air. A is hung from the right-hand side of the balance rather than being placed on top of it. When a glass of water or other liquid is placed so that the body A is immersed in it (see Fig. 2), the side of the scale with the body A will go up. By taking off enough weights on the other side of the scale to re-establish balance, we can determine how much weight the body A lost.

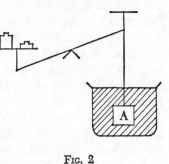

Fig. 2

What is the empirical evidence on which On Floating Bodies *is based?*

In discussing *On the Equilibrium of Planes*, we noted that all the observational evidence on which that book was based was put into the postulates. Is the same thing true here? There is only one postulate prior to the first seven propositions. Archimedes gives us no hint as to how he arrived at it. Is the postulate clear? Is it based on common observational knowledge? Where in the course of the seven propositions is this postulate used?

Archimedes apparently disdains to verify his theoretical conclusions by means of experiments. For instance, he does not make mention of any procedure for testing the loss of weight of a body being weighed in a fluid. We suggested such a procedure above. It is a very simple experiment, and taking into account everything that we know about Archimedes' mechanical and technical proficiency, we must believe that he was perfectly capable of thinking up and designing such an experiment. Why, then, does he choose not to say anything about experiments in his work?

According to Plutarch, Archimedes was contemptuous of the practical applications of mathematics and science. Though this attitude is rare nowadays, we can at least understand it. But unwillingness to concern himself with experimentation for the sake of verifying his theoretical results seems strange in a scientist. Perhaps it is an exaggeration to say that Archimedes was unwilling to make experiments. Yet he seemed to think that they were unnecessary. Do his propositions stand in need of verification?

Is there any sense in which Archimedes' results are based on induction? Would you say that they are generalizations? Are they universal laws of nature?

The following questions are designed to help you test the thoroughness of your reading. Each question is to be answered by giving a page or pages of the reading assignment. Answers will be found on page 223 of this Reading Plan.

1 Suppose a solid one-third as heavy as water is placed in water. How much of it will be submerged?

2 What is Archimedes' definition of a fluid?

3 The shadow of the earth, as observed during eclipses of the moon, is always circular in shape. What does this show about the shape of the earth?

4 Is air a fluid?

5 Is the following statement true or false? "A body totally immersed in water will be acted on by an upward thrust that is equal to the weight of the water displaced."

6 Do bodies weigh less in air than in vacuum?

PTOLEMY

The Almagest

Book I, Ch. (1–8); Book III, Ch. 3–4

Vol. 16, pp. 5–14, 86–96

The motions of the heavenly bodies have played a prominent role in the thoughts and lives of men since the earliest known times. The regularities of the stars in their courses have guided men in the planning and harvesting of food, in hunting and fishing, and other vital activities. The heavenly order and harmony has also played a role in religious life and in thought about the basic nature of the universe. This intense practical and spiritual interest in the heavens accounts for astronomy's becoming the most highly developed natural science of the ancient world.

The work of Ptolemy of Alexandria represents the peak of this development. It combines and perfects the astronomical traditions of his Babylonian, Assyrian, and Greek predecessors. But the dominant influence in *The Almagest* is Greek. Indeed, the title is derived from the Greek word "greatest." From its opening pages we can see that the book is imbued with the

Greek philosophical, scientific, and mathematical genius. Here is a man who is keenly aware of what he is doing, of what kind of science he is trying to construct, and how it relates to other kinds of science.

Ptolemy draws a picture of the world which we no longer accept today. We do not grant that the earth is the center of the planetary system, with the sun circling around it. We do not believe that the heavens necessarily have perfect and regular movements. We do not think of the heavenly bodies as incorruptible and almost divine.

But we do accept many of the purposes and methods of Ptolemy. We pursue astronomy as a science. We believe that the apparently inexplicable must be explained in terms of what we know. We know that we must make hypotheses in science. And as scientists we are never happier than when we can bring the powerful tools of mathematics to bear on a problem in natural science. In short, the heritage which Ptolemy has left us is that the entire physical universe must and can be explored by the mind of man.

Sixth Reading

I

The precise birth and death dates of Ptolemy are not known. But the astronomical observations which he records in *The Almagest* were made in the middle of the second century A.D. This, together with tradition, indicates that he lived from around A.D. 100 to around A.D. 178, during the reigns of the emperors Trajan, Hadrian, Antoninus Pius, and Marcus Aurelius. He worked in or near Alexandria in Egypt. Greek astronomy culminated with Ptolemy; he had no successors, only commentators. Ptolemy remained the greatest astronomical authority until the time of Copernicus (1473-1543), Tycho Brahe (1546-1601), and Kepler (1571-1630). Ptolemy himself, however, leaned heavily on the work of his predecessors— both Greek and Babylonian; undoubtedly he owes his greatest debt to Hipparchus, who lived and worked around 130 B.C.

II

Ptolemy used a great many of Hipparchus' observations of the motions of the sun, moon, planets, and fixed stars. What is more important is that he also took over from Hipparchus the notion that the world is geocentric (i.e., that the earth is its center). In the first eight chapters of Book I, Ptolemy indicates what his picture of the world is. In Chapter 3 he tells us that the "heavens" (that is, the fixed stars) move spherically. The reason that the fixed stars are called "fixed" is, in fact, that they are assumed to be fixed to a large sphere, the "heaven" of which Ptolemy speaks. This sphere and the stars fixed on it rotate once a day about a north-south axis, the northern pole of which is located approximately where the north star— Polaris—is seen.

Chapter 4 contains Ptolemy's statement that the earth "taken as a whole, is sensibly spherical." This means that we are to disregard such minor imperfections in the spherical shape as valleys and mountains. The chapter on the roundness of the earth is very brief and contains none of the fanfare that would accompany a new or unusual opinion. We may take it, therefore, that the sphericity of the earth was generally accepted by Ptolemy's contemporaries. It is not true that, until Columbus, everyone thought that the earth was flat. However, in the general decay of scientific knowledge that occurred during the 1000 years prior to the Renaissance, many of the accomplishments of the ancients, such as this one, were forgotten.

The arguments which Ptolemy advanced in support of the opinion that the earth is spherical are the standard ones still used today. We may add one more: the fact that the shadow of the earth on the moon during a lunar eclipse is always circular indicates that the earth must be spherical. Only the shadow of a sphere is *always* circular. In this connection, see the first proposition of Archimedes' *On Floating Bodies*, Book I (Vol. 11, p. 538a-b).

In Chapter 5, Ptolemy gives his reasons for thinking that the earth is the center of the world. The reasons can be summed up by saying that if the earth were not in the center of the world, then it would have to be off to one side. Such "off-centerness" (eccentricity) would have to be apparent to observation. Thus, if the earth were to the north of the center of the universe, then the celestial northern "hemisphere" would not be a true hemisphere, but less than that. Similarly, the portion of the heavens south of the earth would take in more than a hemisphere. This should be detectable by observation. Similar observations should enable us to tell whether the earth is to the east or west of the center of the sphere of the fixed stars.

Ptolemy's next observation is that the sphere of the fixed stars is so vast that relative to it the entire earth is like a point. It may be considered as a point at the center of this sphere, as though it had no dimension at all. Observational evidence backs up this view of the earth's size relative to the sphere of the fixed stars. There is no difference in the relative positions of the stars, no matter from which part of the earth they are observed; that is, there is no parallax. Furthermore, the horizon seems to cut the sphere of the fixed stars in half.

Next, Ptolemy argues that the earth is perfectly motionless. This is not a necessary corollary of the geocentric view of the world. It would be possible to maintain that the earth is in the center of the world, but that it rotates on its axis (thereby producing night and day). As a matter of fact, Ptolemy recognizes that some people have held this very view:

... And it seems to them there is nothing against their supposing, for instance, the heavens immobile and the earth as turning on the same axis from west to east very nearly one revolution a day ... (p. 12a)

And he even admits a few lines later that

... as far as the appearances of the stars are concerned, nothing would perhaps keep things from being in accordance with this *simpler* conjecture ... (p. 12a, italics added)

Ptolemy argues against a motion of the earth, not from astronomical reasons, but from physical ones. He argues that if there were a motion of the earth, then it would be noticeable. For instance, the rapid motion of the earth would result in the air around the earth seeming to move the other way. Modern physics, of course, would say that the atmosphere of the earth rotates with the earth. Thus the motion of the earth produces no relative (and therefore detectable) motion of the atmosphere. As a matter of fact, in the last paragraph of Chapter 7, Ptolemy envisages that all terrestrial bodies and the earth's atmosphere are carried around by the earth, but he dismisses this possibility on what seem to be quite insufficient grounds. Nowadays we ascribe to inertia that everything on the earth, fixed or not, turns around with it. For instance, inertia is the reason that a body thrown straight up into the air lands where it started; the earth does not move out from under it.

We see that Ptolemy actually had within his grasp all the ideas of modern astronomy: he knew that the earth is round;

he envisaged the possibility of the daily rotation of the earth; he was able to conceive, though not to accept, the principle of inertia; and we know that, hundreds of years before Ptolemy, the heliocentric theory (that the sun is the center of the universe) had already been put forth. Archimedes in *The Sand-Reckoner* reports that his contemporary, Aristarchus of Samos, maintained that the earth moves around the sun. (See Vol. 11, p. 520a-b.) Nevertheless, 1500 years were to elapse before the heliocentric theory became universally accepted, and 1600 years passed before the principle of inertia became basic in the physical sciences.

Finally, we must note that in Chapter 8 Ptolemy describes the two basic heavenly movements with which he deals. The first is the general motion from east to west which takes place daily. The second is the much slower additional movement which the planets (and in Ptolemy's scheme these include the sun and the moon) perform from west to east. In the case of the sun this second movement takes one year to be completed; in the case of the moon, approximately twenty-nine days. It is, of course, this second, contrary movement which gives the planets their name, which means "wanderers," and it is also the movement to the explanation of which most of the *Almagest* is devoted.

III

We must now investigate the fundamental purpose which guides Ptolemy's work. Ptolemy inherited a great many observations of celestial phenomena from Hipparchus; he himself added many more such observations. What is observed, of course, is the position of a celestial body, at a given time; many such observations trace the motion of the body across the heavens. A first, but minor, aim of Ptolemy's astronomical work is the compilation of enough observations to make tables that indicate the position of a celestial body at a given time either in the past or in the future. Ptolemy praises Hipparchus for his care and accuracy as an observer:

And so I consider Hipparchus to have been most zealous after the truth . . . especially because of his having left us more examples of accurate observations than he ever got from his predecessors. (p. 272a)

But Ptolemy wanted to do more than merely collect records of astronomical phenomena. What he was interested in was the *explanation* of these phenomena.

The notion that phenomena need explaining is a curious one. An explanation is required when something is strange, unintelligible, or contrary to expectations. But when it has been set down that, say, the planet Mars is at such and such a place in the heavens at such and such a time, what remains to be explained?

To understand the need which Ptolemy feels to explain the planetary and other celestial appearances, we must note that Ptolemy, and ancient astronomers generally, thought that celestial bodies were different from terrestrial ones and should, therefore, be treated in a different manner. Astronomy is, for Ptolemy, a science concerned with almost divine beings. In fact, Ptolemy tells us that he took up the study of astronomy because it is

. . . concerned with the study of things which are always what they are, and therefore able itself to be always what it is—which is indeed the proper mark of a science—because of its own clear and ordered under-standing, and yet to cooperate with the other disciplines no less than they themselves. For that special mathematical theory [i.e., astronomy] would most readily prepare the way to the theological, since it alone could take good aim at that unchangeable and separate act, so close to that act are the properties having to do with translations and arrangements of move-ments, belonging to those heavenly beings which are sensible and both moving and moved, but eternal and impassible. (p. 6a)

Notice especially the description of the "heavenly beings" (i.e., stars and planets) in the last sentence. They are sensible, that is, they can be perceived by the senses, and they move. However, they are eternal and impassible; that is, they are not changeable, except for the change in place which they undergo as they move.

The conception of heavenly bodies as eternal and not subject to any change except locomotion is derived from Aristotle's view of the universe. In the book entitled *On the Heavens*, Aristotle argues that all terrestrial bodies are made up of four elements, namely, earth, water, fire, and air. These simple elements have simple motions that are natural to them: earth and water naturally move downward; fire and air naturally move upward. Celestial bodies, however, are not made up out of these four elements, nor is upward or downward motion natural to them. Their natural motion is circular, and they are made up out of a new fifth element. Aristotle concludes his proof that there is a fifth element as follows:

On all these grounds, therefore, we may infer with confidence that there is something beyond the bodies that are about us on this earth, different and separate from them; and that the superior glory of its nature is proportionate to its distance this world of ours. (Vol. 8, p. 360d)

Ptolemy's contention that the heavenly bodies suffer no change is also derived from Aristotle:

It is equally reasonable to assume that this body will be ungenerated and indestructible and exempt from increase and alteration, since everything that comes to be comes into being from is contrary . . . If then this body can have no contrary . . . nature seems justly to have exempted from contraries the body which was to be ungenerated and indestructible. (Vol. 8, p. 361b-c)

Now let us return to the problem of "explaining" the celestial appearances. What bearing does the character of the heavenly bodies as eternal, unchangeable, and naturally moving with a circular motion, have on this problem? The astronomer's task, as Ptolemy conceived it, arises precisely because the appearances—that is, the observed motions of the heavenly bodies—do not bear out what Aristotle so confidently affirms and what Ptolemy unquestioningly accepts. Astronomical observations, either Hipparchus' or Ptolemy's own, do not show that all the heavenly bodies move in perfectly circular paths. Instead, they reveal that the sun, the moon, and the planets move in complicated motions across the heavens—sometimes forward and sometimes back, sometimes fast and sometimes slow.

It is unthinkable to Ptolemy that such irregularity and imperfection can really belong to the planets' movements. (We here include the sun and the moon among the planets, as Ptolemy did.) Ptolemy, therefore, distinguishes between the *appearance* and the *reality* of planetary movement. The movement appears to be irregular, but it is really regular. The task of "explaining the appearances" then consists in finding the regular movements which the planets "really" make and in showing that these movements would, in fact, produce the irregular movements which they appear to make.

Ptolemy makes this very clear in Chapter 3 of Book III, when he first begins to deal with the sun's movements. The chapter is entitled "On the Hypotheses Concerning Regular and Circular Movement." It begins as follows.

Since the next thing is to *explain* the apparent irregularity of the sun, it is first necessary to assume in general that the motions of the planets in the direction contrary to the movement of the heavens are all regular and circular by nature, like the movement of the universe in the other direction. That is, the straight lines, conceived as revolving the stars or their circles, cut off in equal times on absolutely all circumferences equal angles at the centres of each; and their *apparent* irregularities result from the positions and arrangements of the circles on their spheres through which they produce these movements, but no departure from their *unchangeableness* has *really* occurred in their nature in regard to the supposed disorder of their appearances. (p. 86b, italics added)

Ptolemy's efforts, therefore, are always directed to finding combinations of uniform circular movements, which will produce the appearances that we actually observe. He shows great ingenuity in devising circles, which are of different sizes and turn with different (but uniform) speeds, and in combining their motions so that the most irregular apparent motions may be thought of as made up of them. In the next section we shall see how Ptolemy explains the irregular motion of the sun by means of regular circular motion. This actually is a very simple case, but it will illustrate the principles which Ptolemy employs. As an example of the ingenuity with which uniform circular motions were combined, by Ptolemy and his followers, to explain apparent irregular movements, we may mention that even motion in a straight line can be thought of as resulting from two circular movements. A proof of this is given by Copernicus. (See p. 629b.)

IV

Let us now examine Ptolemy's way of explaining apparent irregularity in the simplest case, that of the sun. The apparent irregularity consists in the fact that the motion of the sun is not always uniform (sometimes the sun moves faster in one period of time than in another), and in the fact that the four seasons are not exactly equal to one another. The sun's motion can be explained by either of two hypotheses, Ptolemy tells us, which are exactly equivalent.

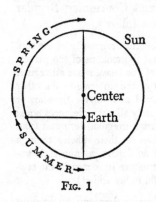

FIG. 1

The *first* hypothesis assumes that the sun moves uniformly in a circle, but that the earth is not located at the center of this circle. Thus the viewer on earth, because of his eccentric location, sees apparently irregular motion. At the same time, this eccentricity will cause the seasons to be unequal in length also. This is a rather simple hypothesis and Ptolemy later on actually adopts it.

The same appearances can also be obtained by a *second* hypothesis. Because this second hypothesis involves an "epicycle," a feature that is characteristic of Ptolemaic astronomy and which is used in explaining the apparent motion of the planets, we shall briefly review it

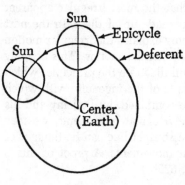

FIG. 2

here. On this hypothesis, we draw a circle around the earth as center. The sun, however, does not move on this circle. Instead, this circle carries on it another little circle. The *carrying* circle is called the "deferent" while the *carried* circle is called the "epicycle." The center of the epicycle, on the deferent, moves uniformly about the earth. The sun is conceived as moving uniformly on the epicycle. The angular speed of the center of the epicycle (measured with respect to the earth) and the angular speed of the sun (measured with respect to the moving center of the epicycle) are equal.

On page 90b, Ptolemy proves that, on both hypotheses, the appearances will be exactly the same. The only requirement is that the radius of the epicycle in the second hypothesis be equal to the eccentricity of the circle in the first hypothesis.

Faced with the equivalence of the two hypotheses, Ptolemy decides in favor of the eccentric circle, since "it would be more reasonable to stick to the hypothesis of eccentricity which is simpler and completely effected by one and not two movements." (See p. 93a.)

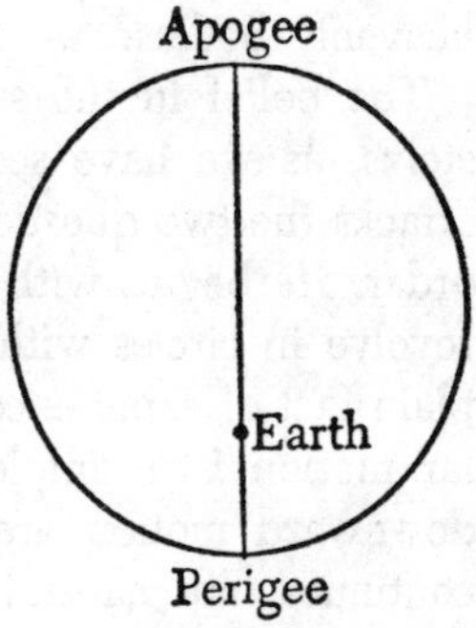

Chapter 4 is given over to calculations. Ptolemy determines the size of the eccentricity of the circle on which the sun moves. Then he turns to the sun's line of apsides. The *line of apsides* is the line drawn from the sun's farthest to the sun's nearest position. The farthest point from the earth is called the *apogee*, the nearest, the *perigee*. (See Fig. 3.) In a heliocentric theory, when the earth is farthest from the sun it is said to be at the *aphelion*, while the point nearest to the sun is the *perihelion*. (See Fig. 4.) In modern theory, the line of apsides is, of course, the axis of the ellipse on which the earth moves about the sun.

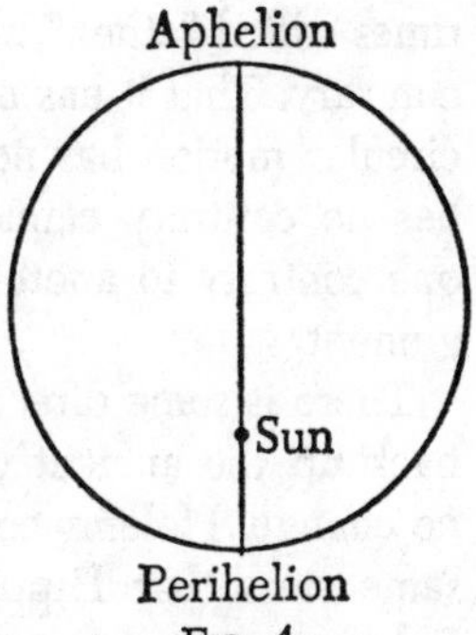

The sun's eccentricity turns out to be one twenty-fourth of the radius, while the apsides are so located that the sun is at the apogee 24° 30′ before it reaches the summer tropic (June 21).

Apogee / Earth / Perigee
FIG. 3

Aphelion / Sun / Perihelion
FIG. 4

V

*What do you think of the principle that all heavenly
motions must be reduced to uniform circular motion?*

There are really two questions here: *first,* is it reasonable
to believe that the heavenly bodies are of a special and noble
nature so that the laws of their motion and change are different from the laws of terrestrial bodies? *Second,* supposing
that the answer to the first question is affirmative, how can it
be shown that only uniform circular motion is suited to the
heavenly bodies?

The belief in the superior nature of the heavenly bodies
stems, as we have seen, from Aristotle. However, Aristotle
attacks the two questions we have listed above in the reverse
order. He begins with the observation that the fixed stars all
revolve in circles with uniform motion. This, of course, is a
plain fact of experience. Aristotle goes on to argue that circular motion is a simple motion, just as upward motion and
downward motion are simple motions. Simple motions, he
continues, are natural to simple bodies. Upward motion is
natural to fire; downward motion, to earth. Circular motion
must be natural to some other element. This element, sometimes called "ether," must be unchangeable, because it has no
contrary. That it has no contrary is evidenced by the fact that
circular motion has no contrary motion. But an element that
has no contrary cannot change, because all change is from
one contrary to another contrary. So much for Aristotle's argument.

There is some direct observational evidence that appears to
back up the ancient view that the heavenly bodies undergo
no change. Ptolemy could point out that he observed the very
same stars that Hipparchus had observed; in addition, the
Babylonians had left records of observations of the same stars
that go back perhaps 2000 years before Ptolemy's time.

Furthermore, without the aid of telescopes no irregularities
could be observed in the celestial bodies. The phases of Venus
could not be seen, nor were the ancients acquainted with the

sudden rise in the intensity of the light of some stars (the novae) and their subsequent decay. Very soon after the telescope had revealed the phases of Venus, the spots of the sun, its rotation, and similar changes, astronomers realized that terrestrial and celestial phenomena are of the same kind, that is, that the heavenly bodies are not exempt from change.

This still leaves unresolved the question why circular motion is the only motion that was thought suitable to the heavenly bodies. Is circular motion more perfect than other motions? Does it more closely approach the supposed unchangeableness of the heavenly bodies in other respects?

Is Ptolemy's Almagest *a work of "celestial mechanics"?*

Celestial mechanics accounts for the heavenly motions in terms of mechanical causes such as attractions, pulls, and similar forces. The *Almagest* contains no such explanations. Ptolemy's view of the heavenly bodies is such that he believes it is in their nature to revolve with uniform circular motion, just as it is in the nature of heavy bodies to move downward in a straight line and with a non-uniform motion. No further explanation is needed why a body moves in a certain way, if we can simply say that it is natural for this body to move in this way.

In contrast, consider Newton's explanation of the motions of the heavenly bodies. Newton's account is definitely mechanical. In Newton's view, uniform circular motion is not natural to the heavenly bodies; some cause, such as an attraction, is needed to explain why the heavenly bodies revolve as they do.

Even if we maintain, as Ptolemy does, that uniform circular motion is natural to the heavenly bodies, there still remains a problem. For the planets do not appear to move with the motion which is said to be natural to them. Why, then, does Ptolemy not explain the apparent planetary motion in terms of mechanical forces which make the planets move otherwise than they naturally would?

To try to account for the planetary motions in terms of

external forces acting on them would violate the principle that these bodies are of a perfect nature. They cannot be subjected to forces, to pushing and pulling; they cannot be considered as merely passive, responding to external causes.

Ptolemy's efforts, therefore, are not directed to finding the forces required to make the heavenly bodies move as they do. Instead, he concentrates on finding the "real" motions, uniform and circular, that must be hidden behind the irregular appearances, but which he knows must be there, because of the nature of the heavenly bodies.

Is a non-mechanical explanation like Ptolemy's as good as a mechanical one? Does all explanation in physics have to be by mechanical causes? Is Ptolemaic astronomy, because it is non-mechanical, also non-physical? Nicomachus considered astronomy to be the sister science of geometry, dealing with "size" in motion. (See Vol. 11, p. 812b.) Does this fit Ptolemaic astronomy?

Are Ptolemy's explanations of planetary motion true or false?

Do not be tricked into answering this question; the question itself is faulty. Throughout his work, Ptolemy makes clear that his explanations are hypothetical in character. Thus Chapter 3 of Book III is entitled "On the Hypotheses Concerning Regular and Circular Movement"; and Chapter 2 of Book IX, the first book dealing with the planets, is called "On the Aim of the Planetary Hypotheses."

A hypothesis is something that is *supposed* to be true, though not *known* to be true. In the statement "If A, then B," the hypothesis is A. On the supposition that A is true something follows, namely that B is true. In the case of Ptolemy's hypotheses, if the heavenly bodies move as he supposes them to move (that is, uniformly in circles, epicycles, etc.), then it follows that they present the appearances which are actually observed.

Let us take the case of the sun as an example. If the sun actually moves on an eccentric circle, with the eccentricity that Ptolemy has calculated and with the line of apsides in the direction that he has calculated, then the sun will appear to move as it does. This is the aim of all of Ptolemy's hypotheses: to find such combinations of regular circular movements that, if the heavenly body in question moved in that fashion, then it would present the appearances which we observe. Such a hypothesis would be said to "explain" the appearances. In the chapter "On the Aim of the Planetary Hypotheses" Ptolemy writes as follows:

Now, since our problem is to demonstrate, in the case of the five planets as in the case of the sun and moon, all their apparent irregularities as produced by means of regular and circular motions (for these are proper to the nature of divine things which are strangers to disparities and disorders) the successful accomplishment of this aim as truly belonging to mathematical theory in philosophy is to be considered a great thing, very difficult and as yet unattained in a reasonable way by anyone. (p. 270b)

A hypothesis in this sense, then, is not true or false; it is successful, or not, in explaining the appearances.

Is there any criterion other than truth or falsity by which hypotheses can be judged? Since more than one hypothesis can often be used (see, for example, the case of the sun's movement), how can one hypothesis be preferred to another? Since neither hypothesis is true, can we say that one hypothesis is more probably true than the other?

Plato, in a famous passage in the *Timaeus*, considers that hypotheses are probable or likely stories concerning reality. In astronomy, Ptolemy thinks they must be used because the real motions of the heavenly bodies escape us. But, according to Timaeus, hypotheses must be used in cosmology, because the creation and constitution of the world is too difficult to permit precise knowledge. Timaeus says to Socrates:

If then, Socrates, amid the many opinions about the gods and the generation of the universe, we are not able to give notions which are altogether and in every respect exact and consistent with one another, do not be surprised. Enough, if we adduce probabilities as likely as any others. ..., (Vol. 7, p. 447d)

Does this statement also fit Ptolemy's hypotheses? Or are the latter's hypotheses exact and consistent? Are they likely stories? If they are only likely stories, how can we say that the "real" motion of the heavenly bodies is circular and uniform?

The following questions are designed to help you test the thoroughness of your reading. Each question is to be answered by giving a page or pages of the reading assignment. Answers will be found on page 223 of this Reading Plan.

1 What are the two primary movements in the heavens?

2 What are the arguments against other than circular motion of the fixed stars?

3 What are the three theoretical sciences that Ptolemy mentions?

4 If a heavenly body, such as the sun, moves in an eccentric circle about the earth, does it move faster or slower at the apogee than at the perigee?

5 At what point is there the greatest difference between the apparent irregular movement of the sun and the "true" regular circular movement?

6 Is the sun farther from the earth in winter than in summer?

7 Nicomachus argued that of all the mathematical sciences arithmetic should be studied first. Does Ptolemy agree?

COPERNICUS

On the Revolutions of the Heavenly Spheres

Introduction and Book I, Ch. 1–11

Vol. 16, pp. 505–532

If you have ever had any doubt about the influence of thought on the world, this work should give you pause. The "Copernican revolution" has probably been of more lasting importance than any of the great political revolutions. Indeed, it is the model event to which other innovators in thought like to refer. Two great writers in our set, Immanuel Kant and Sigmund Freud, also claimed to have wrought Copernican revolutions in human thought through their work.

Kant likened his own work to that of Copernicus, because both overturned previously held conceptions. Copernicus stood the ancient world on its head. Where the earth had been the center of the Ptolemaic universe, the sun now took that place. Where the earth had been immobile in its central position, it now was seen to have both a daily rotation and yearly revolution. The entire world picture was changed by the utterly simple device of exchanging the roles of earth and of sun.

Freud thought that he shared with Copernicus the distinction of having shaken man's confidence in himself. Before Copernicus, it was easy for man to think of himself as the master of the universe and the paragon of creation. He conceived of himself as residing in the center of the world, which displayed its admirable motions as if for his benefit. After Copernicus, however, man saw himself as a small creature, on a small planet, being carried forever around the sun in a universe vastly larger than anything Ptolemy ever thought of.

But this is only one side of the Copernican revolution. Being displaced from the physical center of the world, man began to see that his pre-eminence depended not on his location, but on other attributes. He saw that his dignity lay in the use of his personality, his mind, and his other abilities. Man's physical and intellectual conquest of the world began after the Copernican revolution. If even part of these achievements was due to a discontent engendered by Copernicus' work, it was a discontent worth having.

Seventh Reading

I

This reading contains the essentials of the "Copernican revolution." Aside from mathematical detail, everything that is revolutionary about Copernicus' theory is stated in these 11 chapters. The manner of writing is very undramatic; only the Introduction and Preface give us a hint that these few pages overthrew man's conception of the world and himself. It is now known that the introduction was not written by Copernicus. Still Copernicus must have known that the book would arouse controversy, for he delayed its publication so long that he saw a copy of it only on his deathbed in 1543.

II

Before dealing with what is new in Copernicus' doctrine, it is important to recall what he adopts unchanged from Ptolemy's theory. In Chapter 4 of Book I, Copernicus makes clear that he, as much as Ptolemy, is an adherent of the view that all heavenly motions are essentially circular; any irregularity or non-uniformity is mere appearance. The view that the planets move in paths other than circles—first put forth by Kepler—is as foreign to Copernicus as it would have been to Ptolemy. Indeed, where Copernicus finds that apparent planetary motion deviates from the circular, he employs epicycles in the Ptolemaic manner.

"We must however confess," he writes in Chapter 4,

that these movements are circular or are composed of many circular movements, in that they maintain these irregularities in accordance with a constant law and with fixed periodic returns: and that could not take place, if they were not circular. For it is only the circle which can bring back what is past and over with; and in this way, for example, the sun by a movement composed of circular movements brings back to us the inequality of days and nights and the four seasons of the year. Many movements are recognized in that movement, since it is impossible that a simple heavenly body should be moved irregularly by a single sphere. For that would have to take place either on account of the inconstancy of the motor virtue—whether by reason of an extrinsic cause or its intrinsic nature—or on account of the inequality between it and the moved body. But since the mind shudders at either of these suppositions, and since it is quite unfitting to suppose that such a state of affairs exists among things which are established in the best system, it is agreed that their regular movements appear to us as irregular, whether on account of their circles having different poles or even because the earth is not at the centre of the circles in which they revolve. (p. 514a-b)

III

The great Copernican revolution, of course, consists in substituting a heliocentric system for the geocentric system of Ptolemy. Copernicus advances the view that the sun (helios) rather than the earth (gē) is in the center of the universe. The earth in Copernicus' theory is one of the planets and moves around the sun together with the other planets, Mercury, Venus, Mars, Jupiter, and Saturn. (Common sense and ordinary speech, however, continue to employ the geocentric theory. Copernicus himself, in the quotation above, speaks of the movement of the sun; and to this day we use expressions such as "the sun rises," even though we know that the sun is at rest and that the earth is moving.) In Copernicus' scheme, it is recognized that the moon is not a planet, but a mere satellite of the earth. Figures 1 and 2 illustrate the difference between the two systems.

It should be noted that the way in which the planets and the sun are arranged around the earth was guesswork for Ptolemy. Copernicus, however, derives the order of the six planets from the length of time in which they revolve around the sun; Saturn takes the longest and is farthest away, while Mercury's revolution takes the least time and is the closest of the planets to the sun.

Ptolemy

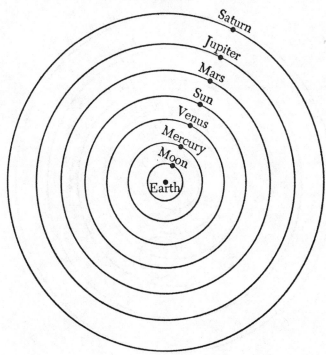

FIG. 1

The beauty of Copernicus' system is its simplicity. By the simple expedient of exchanging the position of the sun and the earth, Copernicus is able to eliminate five epicycles. Each of the five planets (leaving out the sun and the moon) in Ptolemy's system moved on an epicycle which was carried on an eccentric deferent. The function of these epicycles was to explain the *retrograde* motions of the planets. Each planet occasionally slows down in its west-to-east motion, then stands still, and finally goes backward (retrogrades) for a while. Then it slows down in its backward motion, stands still again, and finally resumes its forward motion. When the planet stands

Copernicus

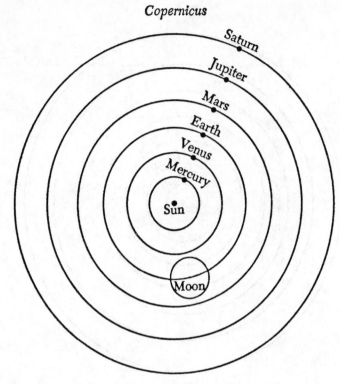

FIG. 2

still, it is said to be at a *station*. Figure 3 indicates how an epicycle explains this phenomenon in a geocentric system.

When the planet is, say, at the bottom of the epicycle (such as C), then, as the center of the epicycle moves from A to B, the planet which was at C moves to E (point C having moved to D). But looking from the earth first at C and then at E, we get the impression that the planet has moved backward.

The exact points of station and retrogradation as well as the extent of the retrogradation will depend on the relative sizes of the epicycle and deferent and on the speed with which the center of the epicycle and the planet on the epicycle move. However, it is clear that to produce an appreciable retrogradation, the epicycle must be large.

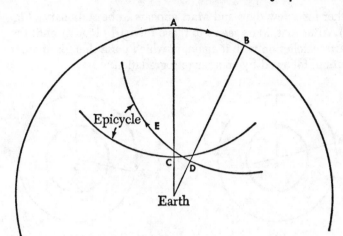

FIG. 3

Under Copernicus' hypothesis, it becomes a much simpler matter to explain retrogradation. Consider, for example, the planet Mars and the earth. The earth moves around the sun more rapidly than Mars (i.e., a martial year is about equal to

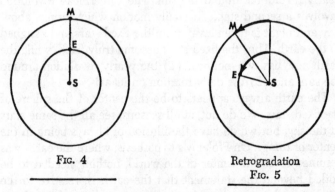

FIG. 4

Retrogradation
FIG. 5

2 terrestrial years). If at some time Mars, the earth, and the sun are in a straight line (Fig. 4), then after a few days the earth will have moved ahead of Mars. Relative to the earth, Mars will have gone backward or retrograded (Fig. 5). When the earth has moved so far ahead of Mars that it is directly opposite it, the motions of Mars and earth seem to cancel each

other for a few days and Mars appears to be stationary (Fig. 6). After that, Mars seems to move forward (Fig. 7) until the earth catches up with it again, at which point there is another station, followed by another retrogradation.

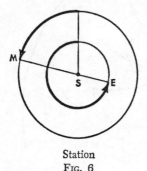

Station
FIG. 6

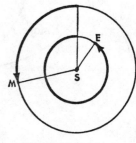

Forward Motion
FIG. 7

IV

So far we have seen that the Copernican system makes the sun the center of the world and the earth a planet with a yearly revolution around the sun. The Copernican revolution involves a second step. The daily motion which brings about day and night is taken away from the fixed stars and assigned to the earth. Thus the fixed stars become truly fixed, while the earth now has two motions: (1) the yearly revolution around the sun, and (2) the daily rotation on its axis.

The earth always appears to be the center of the sphere of the fixed stars. We do not, at all seasons, see all the same stars in the sky, but we do have the illusion of always being in the center of things. On Ptolemy's hypothesis, where the earth was assumed to be the center of the world, nothing needed to be added beyond the statement that the earth is, relative to the fixed stars, like a point. Hence a man on the surface of the earth always seems to be at the center of the world.

In the Copernican hypothesis, however, the earth moves around the sun. The sun is on the average 93,000,000 miles from the earth. Hence the distance between two positions of the earth that are directly opposed to each other is approximately 186,000,000 miles. Yet this vast distance must be as a point relative to the size of the universe, for whether the earth is in one place or the other, it seems to be at the center of the sphere of the fixed stars.

On Ptolemy's hypothesis, therefore, the universe is so big that the diameter of the earth (approximately 8000 miles) is negligible. On Copernicus' hypothesis, however, the universe must be suddenly conceived as so much bigger that 186,000,000 miles are negligible. Thus the universe is now thought to be at least 23,000 times bigger than it had to be on Ptolemy's hypothesis.

This increase in the size of the universe, which is necessitated by the seemingly simple exchange of the roles of earth and sun, is so vast that it is difficult to comprehend. Furthermore, in proportion as the universe is seen to be larger, so man's importance in it appears to be less. Thus Copernicus' hypothesis deals two blows to man's picture of himself as the most important being in creation. First, it removes man from the real center of the world; second, it diminishes man in size and shows him that he is but a minute speck in a vast and empty space.

Sigmund Freud comments on three blows which modern science has dealt to man's pride. The first blow was dealt by Copernicus, the second by Charles Darwin through the theory of evolution, the third by Freud himself through psychoanalysis. In the *General Introduction to Psycho-Analysis,* Freud writes as follows:

Humanity has in the course of time had to endure from the hands of science two great outrages upon its naïve self-love. The first was when it realized that our earth was not the centre of the universe, but only a tiny speck in a world-system of a magnitude hardly conceivable; this is associated in our minds with the name of Copernicus . . . (Vol. 54, p. 562c-d)

V

What are the similarities and differences between Ptolemy's and Copernicus' methods?

Copernicus' method does not differ greatly from Ptolemy's. Both astronomers emphasize the role of hypothesis in astronomy. In Copernicus' case, we find the strongest statement of this made in the Preface, not actually written by Copernicus himself; but in other parts of the book, it is also perfectly clear that the Polish astronomer as much as the Alexandrian one thought his main task consisted in "saving the appearances."

An obvious likeness between the Copernican and the Ptolemaic methods is the insistence on uniform circular motion as the appropriate motion of heavenly bodies. We have already quoted the passage in which Copernicus indicates that nothing but circular motion will do.

In the Guide to the Sixth Reading, we saw that for Ptolemy there was an intimate connection between the motion of the heavenly bodies (uniform and circular) and their physical character (unchangeable). Copernicus shares Ptolemy's belief in the godlike and perfect nature of the heavenly bodies. Thus he refers at the very beginning of the work to "the godlike circular movements of the world and the course of the stars" (p. 510a). And in Chapters 7 and 8, he rehearses Aristotle's argument that a simple movement belongs to simple bodies. He arrives, however, at a result different from Ptolemy's, in that he concludes that the earth must have a circular motion and cannot be at rest. But without doubt Copernicus is still in the Aristotelian tradition of physics, just as Ptolemy was.

Another significant characteristic common to Copernican and Ptolemaic astronomy is that both are non-mechanical. In this respect, too, Copernicus is still on the side of the ancients. Less than 100 years later, Kepler and Galileo introduced mechanical, physical notions into astronomy.

By calling Copernicus' astronomy non-mechanical, we mean that no attention is paid to any forces, attractions, or repulsions between the heavenly bodies. No cause is assigned for the heavenly motions except the alleged fact that uniform circular motion is natural to heavenly bodies. He is content to save the appearances. Neither Ptolemy nor Copernicus is concerned with why or how the heavenly motions are accomplished. By contrast, after 1600, all of astronomy's efforts became directed to these problems.

Can the Copernican hypothesis be confirmed by experimental or observational evidence?

Copernicus presents and defends his theory without the aid of any evidence drawn from experiment or observation. No such evidence was available to him. Nowadays, however, there is ample evidence for the validity of his theory that (1) the earth has a daily rotation, and (2) the earth makes an annual revolution around the sun. We shall present one piece of confirmatory evidence for both parts of the theory.

The rotational motion of the earth is confirmed by the *Foucault pendulum.* The demonstration was first made in 1851 by J. B. L. Foucault. He employed a very long pendulum suspended in such a way that it could move independently of the structure from which it was suspended. A pendulum always performs its oscillations in the same plane (unless forced to deviate by some outside force). The Foucault pendulum, thanks to its suspension, is subject to no deviating force and so maintains its oscillations in the same plane. Meanwhile, however, the earth rotates under it. Hence the Foucault pendulum *appears* to change its plane of oscillation. This rotation of the pendulum's plane of oscillation can be observed.

A striking confirmation of the fact that the earth is a planet and that the orbits of Mercury and Venus are within the orbit of the earth is indicated by the fact that, if this is the case, then Venus and Mercury must have *phases* as seen from the earth. Venus must sometimes be full, sometimes new, sometimes waxing and sometimes waning, just like the moon. In Fig. 8, Venus is in the first quarter; this should be visible from the earth. That Venus actually does have phases was discovered by Galileo by means of his telescope. This led Galileo to support the heliocentric hypothesis. Kepler refers to the phases of Venus and to

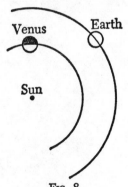

FIG. 8

Galileo's discovery of them when he discusses the evidence for the heliocentric theory. (See Vol. 16, p. 908.)

Without the aid of the Foucault pendulum or the telescope (neither of them possessed by Copernicus), is there any way of judging between Copernican and Ptolemaic hypotheses?

Both hypotheses explain the appearances. Both are able to predict eclipses and similar celestial events. Neither offers a causal explanation of phenomena. Why, then, should one prefer the Copernican to the Ptolemaic hypothesis?

A possible reason may be found in the fact that Copernicus' theory is much simpler than Ptolemy's. It almost does away entirely with epicycles. Its explanation of planetary retrogradation is neat and simple. Its picture of the universe is more uniform and elegant than Ptolemy's. Are these sufficient reasons for favoring Copernicus' theory? Are there any other grounds? What exactly is a beautiful or elegant hypothesis?

The following questions are designed to help you test the thoroughness of your reading. Each question is to be answered by giving a page or pages of the reading assignment. Answers will be found on pages 223-224 of this Reading Plan.

1 Does Copernicus think that astronomy is to be pursued for the sake of utility as well as for its own sake?

2 What three movements does Copernicus attribute to the earth?

3 Does Copernicus think that there is more land or water in the makeup of the earth?

4 In Copernicus' view, is the world finite or infinite in size?

5 What is the shape of the "world"?

6 What are the arguments against Venus' motion on an epicycle, as Ptolemy conceived it?

KEPLER

Epitome of Copernican Astronomy

Selections from Books IV and V

Vol. 16, pp. 845–853, 857–860, 887–888,
907–908, 928–933, 964–967, 983–985

Johannes Kepler is the first modern scientist whom we encounter in this Reading Plan. Although the Copernican revolution upset the ancient views of astronomy, Copernicus cannot be truly called a modern; he still clung to many of the concepts and prejudices of antiquity. Kepler, too, wrought a revolution, and it propelled astronomy headlong into modernity.

It is often said that modern times began in 1600. This is certainly true in the field of science. Kepler's *Epitome,* published in 1618, marks the turning point in astronomy. In physics, it came with Galileo's *Two New Sciences* (1638), in biology with Harvey's *Motion of the Heart and the Blood* (1628), in mathematics with Descartes' *Geometry* (1637).

Kepler's genius lay in his imagination. He was able to free himself from the mass of detailed observations and see things in the heavens that no one before him had noticed. Whereas astronomers for hundreds of years had seen nothing but circles in the heavens, Kepler could see that the planets move in ellipses. The other planetary laws were similarly waiting to be discovered by a mind that was not afraid to take chances. To be sure, that same powerful imagination sometimes led Kepler into fancies where sober scientists have not followed him. Thus, he imagined that the average distances between the sun and the planets corresponded to the radii of spheres inscribed in, and circumscribed about, the five regular solids. He also thought that certain planetary movements give rise to musical harmonies.

Even in his errors, Kepler was grandiose. He was not content with anything less than a system that would encompass the entire universe. He was perhaps the last astronomer who attempted such a sweeping task.

I

Kepler (1571-1630) lived in troubled and turbulent times; during the last years of his life the Thirty Years' War raged. His personal life was marred by sickness and death in his family, and by continual poverty. More details are given in the biographical note. (See pp. 841-842.)

Kepler is a more imaginative writer than either Ptolemy or Copernicus; his style is more grand. His works are much more voluminous than those of Ptolemy or Copernicus. In addition to the *Epitome*, Kepler also wrote *The Harmonies of the World* (Book V of which is included in Volume 16), as well as the large and important *Commentaries on Mars*. In addition, he is the author of astronomical tables, works on optics, and books on astrology.

The *Epitome* was intended as a popular work, giving the highlights of Kepler's system. He writes in dialogue form which indicates that Kepler intended the book to be read by laymen as well as by professional astronomers. The *Epitome* took the place of a much larger projected work, which was supposed to comprehend the entire scheme of the heavens. Insoluble difficulties with lunar theory, however, forced Kepler to give up this plan and settle for the *Epitome* instead. It is interesting to note that lunar theory continued to bother astronomers; even Sir Isaac Newton noted in his Preface to the *Mathematical Principles* that his own account of the lunar motions was still imperfect.

II

Kepler is famous for his three laws of planetary motion. The *first* law (see pp. 964-967) states that the planets move in ellipses (not circles) around the sun; one of the foci of the ellipse

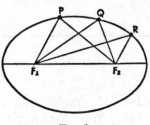

is occupied by the sun, the other focus is in empty space. An ellipse is an oval figure (see Fig. 1). There are various equivalent definitions of it; the following is one of them. An ellipse is a closed curve such that, for any point on it, the sum of the distances from this point to the foci is constant. If the curve in Fig-

FIG. 1

ure 1 is an ellipse, then $PF_1 + PF_2 = QF_1 + QF_2 = RF_1 + RF_2$. F_1 and F_2 are the two foci of the ellipse.

The *second* law (see pp. 983-985) tells us how long the planet takes to traverse any portion of its orbit. For Ptolemy and Copernicus this matter was simple. Since the orbit was composed of circles and since motion on the circles was uniform, the length of time a planet takes to traverse a given arc of a circle is simply proportional to the length of that arc. It takes one and a half times as long to traverse an arc of 45° as it takes to traverse an arc of 30°, and twice as much time to traverse an arc of 60° as it does an arc of 30°.

In an elliptical orbit, things are much more complicated. Different parts of the ellipse curve unequally, and it is not possible to measure the length of any part of the elliptical orbit simply in terms of the angle at the center, as can be done in a circle. Furthermore, the planet moves with varying speed on its orbit, so that equal portions of the ellipse are not traversed in equal times. Kepler discovered, largely through

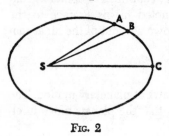

painstaking work on the planet Mars, the following remarkable fact: the time spent by this planet in traversing a part of its elliptical orbit is proportional to the area swept out by the line drawn from the sun to the planet. If, for instance, the area SAB (in Fig. 2) is one

FIG. 2

third of the area SBC, then the planet will take one third as long to travel from A to B as it does to travel from B to C.

Kepler's *third* law (see pp. 887-888) concerns two or more planets. Kepler established that a definite relationship exists between the periodic times of the planets (the length of time for one revolution around the sun) and their distances from the sun. Since the first law tells us that planets move in ellipses, the actual distance of a planet from the sun varies in the course of a revolution. The "distance" which the third law employs, therefore, is the average, or mean, distance of the planet from the sun. The greater the mean distance of a planet, the greater its periodic time; that is, the slower it moves. The third law tells us more than this, however; it gives a numerical relation between distance and time. If the periodic times of two planets are T_1 and T_2, and if their mean distances from the sun are R_1 and R_2, then the law is that

$$\frac{T_1^2}{T_2^2} = \frac{R_1^3}{R_2^3}$$

The squares of the periodic times of two planets are to each other as the cubes of their mean distances from the sun. You may sometimes find the third law expressed in different but equivalent terms, such as that the periodic times are to each other as the three-half powers of the distances:

$$\frac{T_1}{T_2} = \left(\frac{R_1}{R_2}\right)^{3/2}$$

We can illustrate this law in the case of earth and Mars. The periodic time of earth is one year; that of Mars, 1.881 years. $(1.881)^2 = 3.53$, while the square of 1 is, of course, 1. Hence the square of the periodic time of Mars is to the square of the periodic time of the earth as

$$\frac{3.53}{1} = 3.53$$

If the distance of the earth from the sun (which actually is 93,000,000 miles) is called 1, then the distance of Mars from the sun (which actually is 141,700,000 miles) will be 1.524. The cube of 1.524 is 3.539, while the cube of 1 is, again, 1. Hence the cube of the distance of Mars is to the cube of the distance of the earth as

$$\frac{3.539}{1} \text{, which equals } 3.539$$

Let us take another example. The distance of Jupiter from the sun is 483,900,000 miles, while the distance of Mars from the sun is, as stated above, 141,700,000 miles. Now

$$\frac{483,900,000}{141,700,000} = \frac{5.203}{1.524}$$

And taking the cubes of these, we find that

$$\frac{(5.203)^3}{(1.524)^3} = \frac{140.8515}{3.539} = 39.799$$

The periodic time of Jupiter is 11.862 years, while the periodic time of Mars, as stated above, is 1.881 years. Taking the squares of these, we find that

$$\frac{(11.862)^2}{(1.881)^2} = \frac{140.7070}{3.53} = 39.86$$

Again Kepler's third law is strikingly illustrated. (The values for the periodic times and mean distances of the planets are taken from the article PLANETS in *Encyclopaedia Britannica*.)

III

Kepler's achievement involves much more than the substitution of ellipses for circles. If that were his only achievement, he would merely have replaced one geometrical figure with another in describing the planetary paths. But Kepler deliberately and self-consciously rejects the *principles* of traditional astronomy. He himself discusses this matter in Book IV, Part III, Section I, "The Causes of the True Irregularities" (pp. 929-933).

First he states the traditional view.

The ancients wished it to be the office of the astronomer to bring forward such causes of this apparent irregularity as would bear witness that the true movement of the planet or spheres is most regular, most equal, and most constant, and also of the most simple figure, that is, exactly circular. And they judged that you should not listen to him who laid down that there was actually any irregularity at all in the real movements of these bodies. (p. 929a)

Kepler does not reject this view altogether. He agrees that there must be regularity in the planetary movements, that the periodic times of the planets must have some relation to each other and to the path of the planet. But he rejects as illegitimate the conclusion that therefore the planets' movements must be circular and uniform. And this, we remember, was a cardinal point with both Ptolemy and Copernicus.

Kepler's attack on ancient astronomy is systematic. He lists four arguments given by the ancients which were supposed to establish that planetary motion had to be uniformly circular. We have encountered these reasons in the two previous readings. Kepler rejects all four reasons as either false or inconclusive.

The first argument of the ancients was that the heavenly bodies are of a special nature. Whereas all terrestrial things are, according to ancient physics, made up of the four elements (earth, air, fire, and water), the celestial bodies are made up of the fifth element ("quintessence"). This fifth element is of such perfection that the heavenly bodies suffer no change or irregularity. That is why only uniformly circular motion is appropriate for them.

The second argument is that the causes of planetary motion are minds or "intelligences" (something like angels), which are attached to the planets. "And accordingly . . . the figures of the movements, on account of the very nature of the minds, are most perfect circles" (p. 930b).

The third argument is also derived from a principle of ancient physics and is related to the first reason. The principle is that every body has a motion proper to it. Heavy bodies have a natural downward motion, while light bodies move naturally upward. (Heavy bodies are preponderantly composed of earth, while fire is the preponderant element in light bodies. The natural movement of earth is down; that of fire, up.) Now the heavenly bodies are not made up of either earth or fire, or water, or air, but of the fifth element. This fifth element must have a motion proper to *it;* and its natural motion is uniform circular motion.

The fourth argument is that the circle is the most perfect geometrical figure and so necessarily is appropriate to the most perfect bodies—the heavenly ones.

Now what are the arguments by which the "modern" Kepler rejects these "ancient" time-honored reasons?

Kepler is sufficiently steeped in the tradition to agree that the heavenly bodies are of a special nature, but he insists that they are *bodies* nevertheless. Some irregularity in their motion, he says, is accounted for simply by their being bodies. As bodies, they are subject to laws of motion. For instance, Kepler maintains that there is a certain amount of attraction between two heavenly bodies and that this attraction is a function of the distance between them.

The notion of an attraction between bodies is something quite new. Kepler likens this attraction to magnetism and explains it in a highly complicated way. Nevertheless, there is here an anticipation of Newton and his law of universal gravitational attraction between bodies. The notion that magnetism, a terrestrial phenomenon, can be applied to heavenly bodies is an idea foreign to the ancient astronomers, for it implies that the heavenly bodies are constituted just like the terrestrial ones.

In refuting the second reason of the ancients, Kepler again uses modern notions. He denies that the heavenly bodies are moved by "intelligences" or minds. "A truer philosophy," he points out, referring to his own doctrine, places the cause of the motion in "the natural power of the bodies" (p. 931a). The combination of a body's own natural power with the attraction of other bodies results in motion that is less perfect than circular motion.

The third argument is dismissed simply. Kepler grants that heavy bodies move down, light ones up. And, furthermore, heavenly bodies traverse a closed path; i.e., they always return to where they started. But this, Kepler says, does not show that the path must be circular, but merely that it must be a closed curve, such as the ellipse also is.

With respect to the fourth argument, Kepler grants that the circle is the most perfect figure. He denies, however, that it is appropriate to planetary motion, since planets are bodies and are not, as the ancients thought, moved by "intelligences."

IV

Was there a Keplerian revolution?

Although the phrase "Copernican revolution" is frequently used, we never speak of a "Keplerian revolution." Yet Kepler's work differs in many respects from Copernicus', and is more radical in its innovations.

Copernicus, we saw, greatly changed the content of astronomy, but hardly brought about any changes in method. He put the sun in the center of the world and he said that the universe had to be immensely larger than had been believed; but he retained the hypothesis of uniformly circular motion and all that it implies.

Kepler, on the other hand, does not make too many changes in the content of Copernican astronomy. In fact, the book we read is called an epitome of Copernican astronomy. Kepler's changes are in method and in his approach to astronomy.

He rejects the notion that the heavenly bodies are unchangeable.

He rejects the view that the "real" motion of the heavenly bodies must be uniform and circular.

He makes, in fact, no distinction between real and apparent celestial motion, but deals with the observed phenomena.

He treats celestial and terrestrial phenomena as essentially the same. This is shown by his willingness to conceive of magnetic attraction between celestial bodies. He knows about and recognizes the significance of sunspots and the phases of Venus.

He is not content with saying that the celestial motions are natural. He insists on trying to explain them in terms of attraction (such as magnetism) and other forces.

Which is the more radical change—that from Ptolemy to Copernicus or that from Copernicus to Kepler? Is a change in method more significant than a change in the substance of a scientific discipline?

We have several times called Kepler a "modern scientist." Are there also traces of ancient astronomy in his work?

What is the character of Kepler's reasoning?

We have already compared Kepler's method with that of Copernicus and Ptolemy. Now, however, we want to compare his method with that of other scientists and mathematicians.

Does Kepler make use of experiments and observations? Does he use the method of induction to arrive at general statements? Are there any generalizations in this reading?

Why does Kepler not arrange his work in Definitions, Postulates and Propositions like Archimedes? Is the work at all mathematical in character?

Are any of Kepler's arguments based on final causes? Does he ever use the design and purpose of the universe as the reason for why things are as they are?

Is there any trace of the Pythagorean strain in Kepler's work?

The following questions are designed to help you test the thoroughness of your reading. Each question is to be answered by giving a page or pages of the reading assignment. Answers will be found on page 224 of this Reading Plan.

1 What are the principles of Copernican astronomy as enumerated by Kepler?

2 Kepler gives two major arguments for locating the sun in the center of the world. What are they?

3 Kepler asserts that the sun turns on its axis. How long does he say one rotation takes?

4 What does Kepler consider his major deviation from the Copernican principles of astronomy?

5 Did Kepler know that Venus has "phases" like the moon?

6 How does Kepler argue against any motion by the fixed stars?

7 Who are the three men upon whose doctrines Kepler founds his system?

GALILEO

The Two New Sciences

Third Day, Selections

Vol. 28, pp. 197–208

In many respects, Galileo typifies the man of science. His devotion to the pursuit of learning and to the truth was so great that he let nothing stand in its way. All the stories about him—and they are many—indicate that he had but one interest throughout his life, namely, the investigation of nature. In the cathedral at Pisa, instead of listening to the service, he watched the chandeliers swing regularly and so discovered the isochronism of pendulums. While he was a lecturer at the University of Pisa, instead of paying attention to the niceties of academic life with an eye to advancement, he so infuriated his fellow professors that he had to resign. When he was accused of heresy because of his adherence to the Copernican system, he recanted, but —so the story goes—rose from his knees, stamped on the ground, and exclaimed, "Nevertheless it [the earth] moves." The story is no doubt apocryphal, but it serves

117

to show how uncompromising with the truth Galileo is traditionally pictured.

The book before us records his major discoveries concerning the motion of bodies. But this is no dry textbook, full of the jargon of specialists. It is cast in the form of a dialogue between three men who, though well educated, are not themselves scientists. The pace of the work is leisurely, and very little of it is highly technical. It is punctuated with examples drawn from everyday life, and the wishes of the company for additional discussion are almost always heeded.

The Two New Sciences reminds us that before the 20th century the pursuit of science was thought to be not just the business of a few specialists, but of every educated person. Perhaps we will return to this ideal some day.

I

Perhaps the best-known fact of Galileo's life is his trouble with the Inquisition because he upheld the truth of the Copernican astronomical system. Although Galileo was an ardent and imprudent champion of this doctrine, he contributed less to astronomy than to other sciences. Indeed, his theoretical discoveries in astronomy are negligible. In this respect he was far surpassed by his contemporary, Kepler. However, Galileo invented and built the first astronomical telescope; this was of immense practical help to astronomy. It enabled him to discover four of Jupiter's satellites, as he tells us in the *Starry Messenger*, and to verify that Venus, like the Moon, has phases. Kepler, you may remember from the last reading, refers to Galileo's discovery of the phases of Venus. (See Volume 16, p. 908.)

Another oft-told story about Galileo has it that he dropped bodies of different weights from the Leaning Tower of Pisa in order to demonstrate that all bodies fall with equal speed. It is doubtful whether the story is true; but it is a fact that Galileo was born in Pisa and for many years studied and taught there.

It is in connection with the fall and motion of bodies that Galileo made his greatest scientific contributions. One of the "two sciences" in the title of the present reading is that dealing with the motions of bodies; the other science is that dealing with the strength of bodies. Mechanics may be said to have received its start from Galileo. He anticipated and paved the way for Newton's more systematic account of the forces involved in the motion of bodies.

The Two New Sciences was published in 1638, five years after Galileo's trial by the Inquisition, and four years before his death at the age of 77. Instead of being divided into books or chapters, the work is divided into four days. It is cast in the form of a dialogue between three persons. These three men—Salviati, Sagredo, and Simplicio—meet and talk on four consecutive days, taking a different subject each day. The dialogue device is soon almost entirely discarded, however. The larger portion of the third day consists of propositions written by "our author," Galileo, and read by Salviati to the other two.

Salviati and Sagredo represent two real friends of Galileo. Filippo Salviati was a Florentine nobleman and a student and co-worker with Galileo; Gianfrancesco Sagredo was a high-ranking Venetian and a staunch friend of Galileo's during the latter's stay in Venice. Simplicio is apparently a fictitious person; he is meant to represent the Aristotelian school of thought. All three persons appear also as the speakers in Galileo's *Dialogue on the Great World Systems*,[1] the work on the Copernican and Ptolemaic theories that aroused the wrath of the Inquisition.

II

The subject of both the Third and Fourth Day is change of position, or motion. Altogether, three kinds of motion are discussed. The Third Day begins with a short section on *uniform* motion. The remaining portion of the third day and all of the fourth day is taken up with the subject of non-uniform motion. Non-uniform motion is divided into two kinds: *natural* and *violent* motion. Natural motion is treated in the Third Day; violent motion, in the Fourth Day. The division can be summed up as follows:

1. Uniform motion. Pp. 197b-200a
2. Non-uniform motion. Pp. 200a-260a, c

---

[1] *Dialogo dei Massimi Sistemi,* translated by Thomas Salusbury. Revised, annotated, and with an introduction by Giorgio de Santillana. Chicago, 1953: The University of Chicago Press.

a. Natural motion. Pp. 200a-237a, c
b. Violent motion. Pp. 238a-260a, c

The notion that some motions are natural and others are violent (i.e., non-natural) obviously goes back to Aristotle. In connection with the astronomical readings, we repeatedly referred to his theory of the natural motions. Thus, downward motion in the Aristotelian scheme is natural to the element earth (and to bodies mainly composed of earth), upward motion is natural to fire, and uniform circular motion is natural to the fifth element composing the heavenly bodies. The motion which is natural to one kind of element is unnatural to another element. Thus, upward motion is unnatural to the element earth. This element, and bodies composed of earth, can move upward only if their natural downward tendency is interfered with by violence.

The section on natural motion in the Third Day deals only with the natural motion of the element earth or bodies composed of earth. In other words, Galileo considers only the downward, falling motion of heavy bodies. He pays no attention at all to the natural upward motion of fire and similar bodies.

Similarly, only the violent motion of heavy bodies is treated in the Fourth Day. This is the motion of projectiles, which results when some impressed force interferes with the downward tendency of a heavy body, so that the body goes upward and curves in a manner contrary to its natural tendency.

III

Galileo is a mathematical physicist. This appellation indicates something about the subject matter he deals with and about the method he employs. Galileo's subject matter is nature (the Greek word *physis* means nature). He investigates the properties and motions of bodies. His method is mathematical. The solution to any problem in physics consists in an appropriate mathematical formula.

The Third Day very clearly illustrates the work of the mathematical physicist. In the section on uniform motion, Galileo begins with a definition. From this definition and four axioms, he derives a number of propositions. The last of these is equivalent to the standard formula for uniform motion:

distance traversed = speed × elapsed time.

With the proof of this proposition, the section on uniform motion ends and the section on non-uniform natural (falling) motion begins.

Here, as in the previous section, Galileo begins with a definition. He writes:

> And first of all it seems desirable to find and explain a definition best fitting natural phenomena. For anyone may invent an arbitrary type of motion and discuss its properties; thus, for instance, some have imagined helices and conchoids as described by certain motions which are not met with in nature, and have very commendably established the properties which these curves possess in virtue of their definitions; but we have decided to consider the phenomena of bodies falling with an acceleration such as actually occurs in nature and to make this definition of accelerated motion exhibit the essential features of observed accelerated motions. And this, at last, after repeated efforts we trust we have succeeded in doing. In this belief we are confirmed mainly by the consideration that experimental results are seen to agree with and exactly correspond with those properties which have been, one after another, demonstrated by us. Finally, in the investigation of naturally accelerated motion we were led, by hand as it were, in following the habit and custom of nature herself, in all her various other processes, to employ only those means which are most common, simple and easy. (p. 200a-b)

Galileo follows this up almost at once with his proposed definition: a motion such that the increments of speed are proportional to the increments of time. This means that during any equal time-intervals equal amounts of speed are added to the motion. Let us look at an example. Suppose that a body falls and that after 5 seconds it attains the speed 15 centimeters per second. It continues to fall and reaches the speed 21 centimeters per second after 2 more seconds (7 seconds from the beginning of the fall). Thus, during 2 seconds the increment of speed was 6 centimeters per second.

The body continues to fall. After a total of 10 seconds, the body reaches the speed of 30 centimeters per second. Let 2 more seconds elapse. Then, according to Galileo's definition, the body will reach the speed of 36 centimeters per second.

Time since the beginning of the fall	Increment of time	Speed attained by body	Increment of speed
0	0	0	0
5	} 2	15	} 6
7		21	
10	} 2	30	} 6
12		36	

FIG. 1

In this way, during 2 seconds (from the 10th to the 12th second), the increment of speed was again 6 centimeters per second. Figure 1 is an illustrative table using these same figures.

The definition that Galileo gives is equivalent to the formula:

$$\text{speed} = \text{acceleration} \times \text{time.}$$

Just as he did in the section on uniform motion, so in this section Galileo follows the definition with a series of propositions that are derived from it. Most of the Third Day, in fact, consists of such propositions and their proofs. The most important of these propositions are the first and second one (pp. 205-206). Stated in formulary manner, they are as follows.

Prop. I: distance traversed = ½ terminal speed × time

   elapsed

Prop. II: distance traversed = ½ acceleration × (time

   elapsed)^2

So far, we have noticed two steps in Galileo's method. First, he proposes a definition. In the case of uniform motion, no justification is given for the definition; and not very much is said in behalf of the definition of natural motion beyond the remark that it fits the "habit and custom of nature" in being "most comon, simple and easy." These definitions we may regard as hypothetical formulations. Galileo apparently found them by genius, instinct, or good luck.

The second step in the method of the mathematical physicist as exemplified by Galileo consists in the mathematical development of the original hypothesis. These first two steps of method are exemplified not only in Galileo's work, but also in that of Archimedes.

There is yet a third step which must be taken, if the method is to be complete. This is the experimental verification of the hypothesis and its mathematically developed consequences. Simplicio requests such verification shortly after Salviati has read the demonstrations of Propositions I and II to the group.

. . . it seems to me, not only for my own sake but also for all those who think as I do, that this would be the proper moment to introduce one of those experiments—and there are many of them, I understand—which illustrate in several ways the conclusions reached. (p. 207d)

Salviati at once assents.

The request which you, as a man of science, make, is a very reasonable one; for this is the custom—and properly so—in those sciences where mathematical demonstrations are applied to natural phenomena, as is seen in the case of perspective, astronomy, mechanics, music, and others where the principles, once established by well-chosen experiments, become the foundations of the entire superstructure. I hope therefore it will not appear to be a waste of time if we discuss at considerable length this first and most fundamental question upon which hinge numerous consequences of which we have in this book only a small number . . . (pp. 207d-208a)

Here Galileo, through the words of Salviati, gives us his own view of his method: mathematical demonstrations are applied to phenomena; and these demonstrations employ principles that have been verified by experiments.

The statement above is significant because it tells us what Galileo believed to be essential to his method. It is just as important, however, to perceive what Galileo did *not* believe to be part of his task. At a certain point in the discussion, Sagredo suggests that they might

. . . obtain a proper solution of the problem discussed by philosophers, namely, what causes the acceleration in the natural motion of heavy bodies? (p. 202a-b)

He and Simplicio get into a rather spirited discussion of this; but, after a little while, Salviati cuts them short in the most summary fashion.

The present does not seem to be the proper time to investigate the cause of the acceleration of natural motion concerning which various opinions have been expressed by various philosophers, some explaining it by attraction to the centre, others to repulsion between the very small parts of the body, while still others attribute it to a certain stress in the surrounding medium which closes in behind the falling body and drives it from one of its positions to another. Now, all these fantasies, and others too, ought to be examined; but it is not really worthwhile. At present it is the purpose of our Author merely to investigate and to demonstrate some of the properties of accelerated motion (whatever the cause of this acceleration may be) . . . (p. 202d)

According to this statement, the investigation of causes does not come within the physicist's purview. All the proposed causes of accelerated motion seem to Galileo to be "fantasies," and their examination "not really worthwhile." Compare this with Aristotle's statement in the *Physics:* after enumerating four kinds of causes, Aristotle adds:

Now, the causes being four, it is the business of the physicists to know about them all . . . (Vol. 8, p. 275b)

We shall encounter disdainful attitudes toward causes again. The real task of physics, according to this attitude, is "to demonstrate some of the properties of accelerated motion (whatever the cause of this acceleration may be.)" Aristotle, of course, would be scandalized by anyone who wanted to investigate the properties of motion without knowing its cause. He would, in fact, maintain that it is impossible to discover the properties of anything without knowing its causes. For Galileo, however, it is a simple matter to find the properties of accelerated motion; it is merely a matter of deducing the mathematical consequences of the definition of such motion.

IV

After defining uniform motion, Galileo adds a "Caution." What is the purpose of it? Is it really necessary?

Here is what Galileo says about the "caution":

> We must add to the old definition (which defined steady motion simply as one in which equal distances are traversed in equal times) the word "any," meaning by this, all equal intervals of time; for it may happen that the moving body will traverse equal distances during some equal intervals of time and yet the distances traversed during some small portion of these time-intervals may not be equal, even though the time-intervals be equal. (p. 197c)

It is easy to give an example of what Galileo is driving at here. Imagine an automobile to be traveling for two hours. Because of varying traffic conditions, the distances it traverses in the four half-hour period are as follows:

| 1st half hour 30 miles | 2nd half hour 15 miles | 3rd half hour 20 miles | 4th half hour 25 miles |

And hence it would be true also that in the two one-hour periods it would traverse the following distances:

| 1st hour 45 miles | 2nd hour 45 miles |

Is the car traveling with uniform motion? If we consider only the one-hour intervals we might be tempted to say it is, since in those two equal time-intervals it traverses equal distances, namely, 45 miles. But if we consider the four equal half-hour intervals, we find that equal distances are not traversed during them. The motion, therefore, is not uniform.

According to this caution, do equal distances have to be traversed by a body traveling with uniform motion, even during tiny time-intervals such as a ten-thousandth of a second?

Keeping in mind this caution, do you think that any uniform motion is found in nature?

How valid is the method of proof that Galileo employs in Proposition I?

Suppose a body to fall from rest and to fall for a length of time *t*. At the end of time t, it has reached a velocity *v*. Then Galileo's Proposition I states that the distance, *s,* which the body has fallen in time t is equal to the distance it would have traversed in time t with a uniform motion whose speed was the mean (average) between the highest and lowest speeds attained by the body.

The lowest speed of the body is, of course, *O*; the highest speed is v. The mean or average of O and v is ½v. In uniform motion, with speed ½v, in the time t, the body traverses a distance, s, such that

$$s = (½v)t$$

or simply

$$s = ½vt$$

The formula is correct. Galileo's proof is brilliant. His method, however, is of dubious validity in spite of—or perhaps because of—its brilliance.

Galileo draws a line AB to represent the time t. Perpendicularly to AB he draws EB to represent the velocity attained, v. He joins AE. Then any line like PQ will represent the speed at time AQ (for we remember that v = at, or that speed is proportional to time). He then bisects EB at F, draws FG parallel to AB and GA parallel to EB. He has no trouble showing that then the rectangle ABFG (½vt) is equal to the triangle ABE. He then assumes that *the triangle ABE is a representation of the distance traversed by the body in time AB*. But why is this so? ABE is a tri-

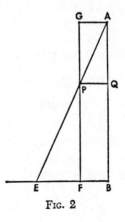

FIG. 2

angle made up of an infinite number of lines like PQ; each of these lines represents the speed of the falling body at the point in time represented by the point on line AB at which it is drawn. Why does a triangle made up of an infinite number of parallels representing speed represent distance?

There is no answer. Galileo's step is unwarranted by anything he has said. Nevertheless, it is true. With brilliant insight, Galileo has anticipated discoveries of the integral calculus. There it can be shown that an area such as ABCD (see Fig. 3) does in fact represent, accurately and numerically, the distance traversed by a body, provided that the line AB represents the time and that a line such as EF represents the speed at time E. Galileo, however, assumes this; he does not prove it. Nor does he have the mathematical tools with which he could prove it.

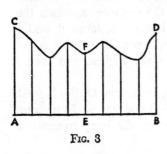

FIG. 3

From $s = \frac{1}{2}vt$ and $v = at$, it follows that
$$s = \frac{1}{2}at^2$$

This is the formula for uniformly accelerated motion. What do you think of a proof such as this one, which uses true but unproved principles? Is the validity of the proposition impaired by the lack of validity of the proof?

Galileo seems to have known intuitively that an area such as ABCD (in Figure 3) represents distance traversed by a body. Is intuition a good substitute for rigor of proof?

What does the experiment with the inclined plane accomplish?

The point at which Simplicio asks about experiments comes after the company has heard Galileo's definition of uniformly accelerated motion and the first two propositions derived from it. "But as to whether this acceleration is that which one meets in nature in the case of falling bodies, I am still doubtful," Simplicio says, and adds that "this would be the proper moment to introduce one of those experiments . . . which illustrate . . . the conclusions reached." (p. 207d)

The purpose of the experiment, therefore, is to show that freely falling bodies in nature have a motion that corresponds exactly to uniformly accelerated motion as defined. The experiment allegedly accomplishes this by showing that when a ball rolls down an inclined plane the distances traversed are to each other as the squares of the times in which the distances are traversed. That, in uniformly accelerated motion, the distances are as the squares of the times is of course precisely what Proposition II tells us.

However, the experiment does not tell us about the motion of a freely falling body, but only about motion of a body down an inclined plane. It indicates that the latter motion is, indeed, uniformly accelerated.

This does not mean that the experiment fails in its purpose. It merely indicates the need for some additional reasoning in order to transfer results obtained with the body on the inclined plane, to the freely falling body. As a matter of fact, the experiment with the inclined plane is still used to verify that the motion of a freely falling body is uniformly accelerated. One reason for this is that it is very much easier to experiment with bodies on an inclined plane than with bodies in free fall.

Can you supply the steps of reasoning that Galileo omitted? Can you use the results on p. 204, which show that the speeds attained by bodies rolling down planes of various inclinations but of the same height, are equal?

For his experiment on the inclined plane, Galileo employed a water clock. As he describes it, is it suitable for his purpose?

Whether or not such a clock is suitable in all respects, it was probably the best kind of timepiece available to Galileo.

The only practical alternative he had was to use his pulse, and that seems less accurate and less easily usable (for the short times involved) than the water clock.

How does Galileo know that the amount of water collected is a measurement of the time? Does the amount of water in the vessel make any difference to the accuracy of the measurement? Is it better to have the water run out of a large or a small opening?

The following questions are designed to help you test the thoroughness of your reading. Each question is to be answered by giving a page or pages of the reading assignment. Answers will be found on page 224 of this Reading Plan.

1 What is the speed attained by bodies rolling down inclined planes of different inclinations but of the same height?

2 Suppose a body falls with uniformly accelerated motion. What relationship do the distances have that are traversed during equal time-intervals (for example, the distances traversed during the first second, the second second, the third second, etc.)?

3 If the bob of a pendulum is raised to a certain height and the pendulum then released, how high will the bob rise on the other side?

4 When a body starts to fall from rest, does it instantaneously acquire a certain speed, or does it pass through all degrees of slowness?

5 What are the axioms required for the discussion of uniform motion?

6 Of what material is the ball that Galileo employed in verifying his theory by the inclined plane experiment?

BACON

Novum Organum

Preface, Book I, Aph. 1–65; Book II, Aph. 1–20

Vol. 30, pp. 105–114, 137–153

The ancient scientists were aware that practical applications might be drawn from their work. Astronomy could and did help the sailor and the farmer in their pursuits. And Archimedes applied his genius to inventing machines of war. But the basic interest of scientists until the Renaissance was *knowledge for its own sake*. To know and contemplate the truth about nature was the essential aim.

Francis Bacon signals the advent of a new era in science. The aim of science for him is power over nature, to bend it to our purposes. Knowledge of how effects are produced is not a theoretical matter, but a means to the know-how that will bring about technological advancement. Science is to be judged not merely by the truth of its statements about the existing world, but by its fruitfulness in producing new facts and new things. For the first time, we hear the modern pragmatic notion of truth forcefully announced.

Also modern is Bacon's cry to make everything new —a new system of the sciences, a new method of inquiry, discoveries of new things. The new is now the good to be aimed at, rather than the traditional, time-honored old. Ever since Bacon's time, the traditional view, the opinion of the "schools," has been suspect in the eyes of scientists.

Bacon himself was a pioneer in building the new scientific attitude. Succeeding centuries developed the towering structure of modern natural science, but he was the true prophet of the coming age. Only in this century has his view of science begun to be challenged. Today we witness the hot debate between the advocates of "basic research" and the advocates of useful knowledge. Bacon is the earliest and perhaps the greatest exponent of the latter view.

I

Francis Bacon (1561-1626) published no work entitled *Novum Organum*. What he did publish, in 1620, was *The Great Instauration*. This book was conceived in a very ambitious manner. The "Plan of the Work" tells us that it was to have six parts. They were as follows:

1 The Divisions of the Sciences.
2 The New Organon; or Directions concerning the Interpretation of Nature.
3 The Phenomena of the Universe; or a Natural and Experimental History for the Foundation of Philosophy.
4 The Ladder of the Intellect.
5 The Forerunners; or Anticipations of the New Philosophy.
6 The New Philosophy; or Active Science.[1]

The *Novum Organum* is, accordingly, merely the second of six parts. What has caused this part to become better known than the whole is the fact that *The Great Instauration* remained largely a projection. Indeed, the "Plan of the Work" is followed by a page on which we read the following: "The first part of the *Instauration*, which comprises the divisions of the sciences, is wanting. But some account of them will be found in the Second Books of the 'Proficience and Advancement of Learning, Divine and Human.'"[2] Then follow the two books of the *Novum Organum*. The third part of *The Great Instauration* was to have been a "Natural and Experimental History for the Foundation of Philosophy"; in its stead,

[1] *The Works of Francis Bacon,* ed. by Spedding, Ellis, and Heath. Boston, 1860-1863. Vol. 8, p. 38.
[2] *Ibid.,* p. 55.

Bacon put a short work entitled *Parasceve* (preparation), which is a "description and delineation" of this history rather than the history itself. The reason for the substitution is that

> . . . a history of this kind . . . is a thing of very great size, and cannot be executed without great labour and expense; requiring as it does many people to help, and being . . . a kind of royal work. It occurs to me therefore that it may not be amiss to try if there be any others who will take these matters in hand.[8]

These three works are all that appeared in 1620. Parts 4, 5, and 6 were omitted altogether (nor were they ever written). Part 3 was a mere sketch of what was promised, while Part 1, as we have seen, was to be replaced by the *Advancement of Learning,* which had already been published in 1605 (although Bacon expanded it, had it translated into Latin, and published it in 1623 under the title *De Augmentis Scientiarum*). Only in Part 2 did Bacon produce something new and complete. Small wonder, then, that he is remembered as the author of the *Novum Organum* and not of *The Great Instauration.*

II

It is perhaps not altogether fanciful to say that the incomplete and fragmentary character of Bacon's major work is to some extent a reflection of his confused and harassed personal life. In the aims of the *Instauration* as in the aims of his own career, Bacon was most ambitious. In both cases, he succeeded only partially. For general information concerning Bacon's life, we refer the reader to the biographical note at the beginning of Volume 30, as well as to the article BACON in the *Encyclopaedia Britannica.*

Almost all of Bacon's life was spent in seeking preferment and position at the Court. Since he was poor and constantly harassed by debts, it was not ambition alone but necessity that drove him to seek favor at the hands of Elizabeth I and James I. He did not succeed well with the Queen, being passed over, in spite of his strong efforts, for both the office of

---

[8] *Ibid.,* p. 353.

solicitor and attorney-general. With the accession of James, Bacon's fortunes improved, though slowly. In 1613, he finally became attorney-general. In 1616, James made him a privy counsellor, and in 1618 he became Lord Chancellor. In July of that year he was made Baron Verulam; and in January 1621, he was created Viscount St. Albans.

The *Advancement of Learning*, published in 1605 near the beginning of James's reign, was dedicated to the King. When, 15 years later, Bacon published *The Great Instauration*, it commenced with an "Epistle Dedicatory" to James. While the dedication of the former work may have been largely in anticipation of favors to come, the dedication of the latter book was no doubt in appreciation of preferment and rank bestowed, for in 1620 Bacon was the first law officer of the kingdom and his position at the court seemed secure.

His fortunes soon declined rapidly, however. In 1621, he was accused of taking gifts or bribes from persons whose suits were pending in Chancery. Bacon at first looked upon these charges as Parliamentary attacks upon himself, since he had been a strong defender of the king's prerogative. He had hopes of defending himself. When, however, he was confronted with a list of twenty-eight charges, he gave up all idea of defense and sent in his "confesion and humble submission." In it he says

I do again confess, that on the points charged upon me, although they should be taken as myself have declared them, there is a great deal of corruption and neglect; for which I am heartily and penitently sorry, and submit myself to the judgment, grace, and mercy of the court.[4]

The sentence pronounced was a fine of 40,000 pounds, imprisonment in the tower, inability to hold any office or a seat in Parliament, and that he should not "come within the verge of the court." The sentence was only partially carried out. The fine was remitted by the king, imprisonment lasted only about four days, and Bacon finally was granted a general pardon. He never again, however, held public office or sat in

---

[4] Quoted in *Encyclopaedia Britannica*, 9th ed., Vol. 3, p. 208c.

Parliament. He devoted the last years of his life to work on *The Great Instauration*, though, as we observed, he came nowhere near completing it. He died on April 9, 1626.

III

What is the great "instauration" that Bacon had in mind? It is a "restoration." Bacon, writing in the third person concerning himself in the Procemium, tells us what he wants to restore:

> . . . he thought all trial should be made, whether that commerce between the mind of man and the nature of things, which is more precious than anything on earth, or at least than anything that is of the earth, might by any means be restored to its perfect and original condition, or if that may not be, yet reduced to a better condition than that in which it now is.[5]

To bring about this restoration requires a drastic move:

> . . . to try the whole thing anew upon a better plan, and to commence a total reconstruction of sciences, arts, and all human knowledge, raised upon the proper foundations.[6]

In this reconstruction, the *Novum Organum* plays a most important part. For the arts and sciences (described and distinguished in *The Advancement of Learning*) are to be rebuilt not in the same old way as Bacon found them handed down from the ancients, but on new and "proper foundations." The *Novum Organum* is the tool whereby Bacon proposes to make the foundations strong and firm.

The old "organum" is Aristotle's *Logic*. The six logical treatises placed at the beginning of Aristotle's works are collectively called the *Organon* or, in Latin, *Organum*. (See the table of contents in Volume 8, p. vii.) The best-known part of Aristotle's logic is the doctrine of the syllogism, or deductive inference. Bacon, in the "New Logic," proposes a new doctrine. According to Bacon's view, scientific inferences should be drawn from nature and should be inductive, not deductive, in character.

It is important to Bacon that the inferences be made directly

---

[5] Works, Vol. 8, p. 17.
[6] *Ibid.*, p. 18.

from nature. Remember that the subtitle of the *Novum Organum* speaks of the "interpretation of nature." The old logic, Bacon maintains, has not had good results because it concerned itself with concepts that were either illusory or at least useless. Syllogism, or deduction, is of no help in interpreting nature; it is but a spinning out of a few truths to great lengths. "The creations of the mind and hand appear very numerous," Bacon writes,

... if we judge by books and manufacturers; but all that variety consists of an excessive refinement, and of deductions from a few well-known matters—not of a number of axioms. (p. 107b-c)

What Bacon is interested in is *discovery*. He wants new natural effects to be found, not old ideas turned around and around.

As the present sciences are useless for the discovery of effects, so the present system of logic is useless for the discovery of the sciences.

The present system of logic rather assists in confirming and rendering inveterate the errors founded on vulgar notions than in searching after truth, and is therefore more hurtful than useful. (p. 107d)

Bacon returned again and again to the point that a logic of discovery must begin from things. We should be interested in things, not words or propositions. The syllogism cannot help us in understanding things.

The subtilty of nature is far beyond that of sense or of the understanding; so that the specious meditations, speculations, and theories of mankind are but a kind of insanity ... (p. 107d)

And so he dismisses the syllogism by saying that "the present system of logic is useless for the discovery of the sciences." (See p. 107d.) Consequently, "Our only hope, then, is in genuine induction." (See p. 108a.)

Induction, unlike deduction, starts from things and sense experience. From instances of observation and experimentation, induction derives conclusions that are more general than the evidence on which they are based. Thus, induction is the means of giving us laws and principles of nature.

Bacon, of course, did not invent the idea of induction. Aristotle, in the *Prior Analytics*, talks about induction and inductive inference. (See Vol. 8, p. 90a-c.) But what Bacon wants to establish is "genuine" induction. Induction as practiced for the most part does not accomplish what it should, he says. This is due to the unskilful manner in which inductions are made. Statements of the greatest generality and abstractness are derived quickly on the basis of scanty evidence. He compares this method of induction with his own, genuine, method:

> There are and can exist but two ways of investigating and discovering truth. The one hurries on rapidly from the senses and particulars to the most general axioms, and from them, as principles and their supposed indisputable truth, derives and discovers the intermediate axioms. This is the way now in use. The other constructs its axioms from the senses and particulars, by ascending continually and gradually, till it finally arrives at the most general axioms, which is the true but unattempted way. (p. 108b)

The wrong, old-fashioned method of induction, Bacon calls the "anticipation of nature," while the true method is the "interpretation of nature." (See Aphorism 26, p. 108d.)

IV

Bacon does not tell us how we are to go about making true and genuine inductions until Book II. The first book for the most part is devoted to warnings about the futility of former methods, and prophesies about the benefits to be derived by applying Bacon's new method. Let us, therefore, skip to the second book and see what his method amounts to. After some preliminary remarks, he gives us an example of his method at work in "the investigation of the form of heat." (See p. 140d.)

In accordance with his repeated exhortation to start from things and to proceed by slow steps, Bacon proposes that the first thing to do in induction is to make a series of three tables. *Table I* is to contain all the instances that the investigator has found which exhibit the quality or nature under discussion. Table I, therefore, is a list of all sorts of things which have been found to be hot. *Table II* contains instances of things which are not hot. This, however, would be too vast an undertaking unless some restriction were placed on these instances. We must list only these instances, Bacon says, where we do not find heat but where, on the basis of the first table, we suspected that we would find it. Thus, since his first example in Table I was that the rays of the sun are hot, he lists as his first example in Table II that the rays of the moon and stars are not hot. *Table III*, finally, notes the extent to which various things exhibit greater or less degrees of heat.

These three tables are collections of instances. *Table IV* (an "Exclusive Table") consists of inferences drawn from the other tables. All the inferences are negative; that is, each of the conclusions is that heat is not something one might have expected. In the first place, heat cannot be something that is found only on the earth (because the sun's rays exhibit heat). Secondly, heat also cannot be something that is only celestial in nature (because fire and other purely terrestrial phenomena exhibit heat). In the third place, heat cannot be due to the delicate texture of bodies (since all sorts of bodies are hot). And so it goes; there are fourteen possibilities that are excluded in this table. "None of the above natures," Bacon concludes, "is of the form of heat; and man is freed from them all in his operation upon heat." (See p. 150c.)

From this, Bacon finally derives the "form or true definition of heat." He writes: "Heat is an expansive motion restrained, and striving to exert itself in the smaller particles." (See p. 152d.)

Bacon's language is old-fashioned; this gives his remarks about heat a certain quaint quality. More than 200 years later, however, when John Stuart Mill turned to the subject of induction in his *Logic* (published in 1843), he followed in Bacon's footsteps. Chapter VIII of Book III is entitled "Of the Four Methods of Experimental Inquiry." Mill is interested in finding the cause of certain phenomena, just as Bacon was interested in finding the cause of heat in different phenomena. Mill develops a number of canons to guide the inquiry. Here is the first Canon.

If two or more instances of the phenomenon under investigation have only one circumstance in common, the circumstance in which alone all the instances agree, is the cause (or effect) of the given phenomena.[7]

---

[7] *A System of Logic*, London, 1952: Longmans, Green & Co., p. 255.

This, of course, is merely a restatement of Bacon's Table I. Similarly, Mill's second canon is but a refinement of Bacon's Table II.

If an instance in which the phenomenon under investigation occurs, and an instance in which it does not occur, have every circumstance in common save one, that one occurring only in the former; the circumstance in which alone the two instances differ is the effect, or the cause, or an indispensable part of the cause, of the phenomenon.[8]

Finally, we can see that Mill's fifth canon corresponds to Bacon's Table III.

Whatever phenomenon varies in any manner whenever another phenomenon varies in some particular manner, is either a cause or an effect of that phenomenon, or is connected with it through some fact of causation.[9]

V

What is Bacon's aim in the Novum Organum?

The study of the laws of thought and the rules of inference is for the sake of better and clearer thinking. Thus, the *Novum Organum* is written principally for the sake of improving the method of induction. Since induction is a method of gaining knowledge from and about nature, the *Novum Organum* contributes to the increase of knowledge.

Bacon adds an additional note. Though induction is for the sake of obtaining knowledge, knowledge itself is to be prized as a means for yet another end—power.

Knowledge and human power are synonymous, since the ignorance of the cause frustrates the effect; for nature is only subdued by submission, and that which in contemplative philosophy corresponds with the cause in practical science becomes the rule. (p. 107b)

This quotation is from the beginning of Book I, Aphorism 3. Bacon returns to the same point at the end of Book I. In Aphorism 129 he describes the kinds of ambition which men have. After mentioning ambition for personal power and ambition for the aggrandizement of one's country, he continues:

... if one were to endeavor to renew and enlarge the power and empire of

---

[8] *Ibid.*, p. 256.
[9] *Ibid.*, p. 263.

mankind in general over the universe, such ambition (if it may be so termed) is both more sound and more noble than the other two. Now the empire of man over things is founded on the arts and sciences alone, for nature is only to be commanded by obeying her. (p. 135c-d)

Bacon's strongest statement along these lines occurs in Aphorism 81.

... the real and legitimate goal of the sciences, is the endowment of human life with new inventions and riches. The great crowd of teachers know nothing of this ... (p. 120b-c)

Most teachers, he continues, are not interested in knowledge as such, but merely in giving clever lectures and acquiring a measure of personal fame. Even those who are genuinely interested in knowledge pursue it in the wrong way.

But if one out of the multitude be found, who courts science from real zeal, and on his own account, even he will be seen rather to follow contemplation, and the variety of theories, than a severe and strict investigation of truth. Again, if there even be an unusually strict investigator of truth, yet will he propose to himself, as the test of truth, the satisfaction of his mind and understanding, as to the causes of things long since known, and not such a test as to lead to some new earnest of effects, and a new light in axioms. (p. 120c)

Bacon clearly asserts that knowledge is not to be pursued for its own sake. "The satisfaction of . . . mind and understanding" is not a proper end of inquiry, nor is it enough to want to know the causes of things. Does Bacon's view of knowledge agree with Plato's or Aristotle's? Why is it wrong to pursue knowledge simply in order to know? Is the position that knowledge must serve utilitarian ends a "modern" view; i.e., is it present in contemporary thought?

Does this issue relate to the controversy about the importance of "basic research" in science as compared to technological advance?

What are the four idols which make the advancement of knowledge difficult?

Bacon names the idols as follows: idols of the tribe, idols of the den (or cave), idols of the market, idols of the theatre. These idols are "false notions which have already preoccupied

the human understanding, and are deeply rooted in it . . .";
and they "so beset men's minds that they become difficult of
access, but even when access is obtained [they] will again
meet and trouble us in the instauration of the sciences . . ."
(See p. 109c.)

The idols of the tribe are those which are inherent in the
tribe of man, those deceptions which are due to the imperfections of human nature (for instance, the illusions derived
from the senses).

The idols of the den are those of each individual. That is,
each person has in his nature certain causes which prevent
him from understanding some things.

The idols of the market are perhaps most familiar to everyone. These are deceptions and illusions that arise from the
association of men with one another. These are prejudices of
class, race, or nation; prejudices and blindnesses shared by
any group.

Idols of the theatre are probably least aptly named. They
are, according to Bacon, prejudices and false opinions that
arise from dogmatic systems of philosophy.

Is Bacon's list of idols exhaustive or can you think of other
idols? Do any of the idols in Bacon's list tend to overlap?
What, for instance, is the distinction between idols of the
market and idols of the theatre?

How is it possible to guard against a deception (like an idol
of the tribe) to which the whole human race is subject? Is
not the hope to avoid such an idol perhaps itself an idol?

Is it realistic to think that all these causes of illusion and
deception can be cured by improved methods of induction?

Was Bacon an accurate prophet of the future course of science?

For the most part, Bacon was absolutely uncanny in his
powers of prediction. He was unacquainted with the work of
the great scientists of the 17th century. He mentions, though
unfavorably, William Gilbert's work on the magnet; but he
did not know the work of Galileo, Pascal, and William Har-

vey, who were his contemporaries. And, of course, the discoveries of Newton, Huygens, Lavoisier, and later scientists were still in the future. In spite of this, Bacon proclaimed that scientific knowledge would conquer nature and that the future was going to be an age of science.

Even Bacon's powers of prediction could not anticipate what has come to pass. In Aphorism 87 he lists what he considers foolish predictions about future accomplishments of science—predictions which by their very outrageousness tend to discredit the achievements of science. "There have been," he writes,

many silly and fantastical fellows who, from credulity or imposture, have loaded mankind with promises, announcing and boasting of the prolongation of life, the retarding of old age, the alleviation of pains, the remedying of natural defects, the deception of the senses, the restraint and excitement of the passions, the illumination and exaltation of the intellectual faculties, the transmutation of substances, the unlimited intensity and multiplication of motion, the impressions and changes of the air, the bringing into our power the management of celestial influences, the divination of future events, the representation of distant objects, the revelation of hidden objects, and the like. (p. 123a-b)

With the exception of the "management of celestial influences" and the "divination of future events," all of these predictions have come true.

The following questions are designed to help you test the thoroughness of your reading. Each question is to be answered by giving a page or pages of the reading assignment. Answers will be found on page 224 of this Reading Plan.

1 Why are anticipations of nature more readily believed than interpretations of nature?

2 What is the greatest obstacle in the way of clear human understanding?

3 What are the dangers that Bacon foresees in uncontrolled empirical philosophy?

4 Does Bacon think that mathematics has a role in physics?

5 What are the two kinds of imperfections in words?

6 How does Bacon distinguish between metaphysics and physics?

7 How does Bacon show that the nature of heat consists in motion?

146

PASCAL

*Account of the Great Experiment
Concerning the Equilibrium of Fluids*

Vol. 33, pp. 382–389

Blaise Pascal was one of those rare persons who attain greatness in seemingly disparate fields of learning. Selections from his works are included both in this reading plan and in the plan on Religion and Theology. It is amazing to see one man so deeply perceptive in both science and religion.

Pascal was master in both fields. It is interesting to note that he no more tries here to provide a religious or intuitive interpretation of nature than he tries elsewhere to offer a scientific or rationalistic interpretation of religion. In this reading, he presents himself to us as an empirical and mathematical scientist, looking for the operative causes of natural things, for patterns of behavior and basic relations that can be observed, measured, and formulated mathematically. He rejects any explanation in terms of ultimate ends or purposes, or any notion that nature has desires and aversions.

"Why does water rise in a pump?" To answer this

question, Pascal proceeds on the assumption that we can account for what takes place in nature only by measuring the variables involved and formulating their relation in exact mathematical terms. Here the relative pressures of air and various liquids at various heights are the variables. Pascal's experiment is a classic one.

Again we are impressed by the simplicity and directness of a great scientific mind at work on what seems a complicated and mysterious phenomenon. It is fascinating and instructive to watch Pascal's mind pushing aside all but the essential factors required to deal with this problem.

I

Blaise Pascal wrote no lengthy treatise on any subject. His best-known work, the *Pensées* (included in Volume 33), is, as the name indicates, a series of fragmentary thoughts and reflections on various subjects. Some are merely a line or two in length; others extend for several pages. All are interesting and display a keen and profound mind. (See the Eleventh Reading in the Religion and Theology Reading Plan for a discussion of the *Pensées*.) Pascal's scientific writings are of a similar fragmentary character. They display Pascal's brilliance in the variety and difficulty of subjects covered.

Pascal from earliest childhood was a gifted student. The story goes that his father deliberately kept him from geometry (lest he become absorbed in it), but that Blaise discovered the subject at the age of 12, and by himself studied and learned the equivalent of the first 32 propositions of Euclid's *Elements*. If any more evidence of his talent in the sciences were needed, we have only to look at the various matters he occupied himself with, and the treatises he wrote, in a life-span of only thirty-nine years.

Much of his adult life was spent on theological problems; indeed, he is reported to have considered geometry as "only a trade." His theological bent is exhibited in *The Provincial Letters* (included in Volume 33). There Pascal takes the Jansenists' side in their controversy with the Jesuits on the question of God's grace. In addition to his work on hydrostatics (of which the *Great Experiment* is a part), Pascal wrote on the method of geometry, developed the theory of probability, and made many purely mathematical discoveries.

His *Treatise on the Arithmetical Triangle* is reminiscent of Nicomachus in its treatment of numbers.

His life-span (1623-1662) places him almost exactly between Galileo and Newton. Although Pascal did not write on the motion of bodies, he was, like Galileo and Newton, a "modern" scientist. He liberated himself from the authority of Aristotle and, again like Galileo and Newton, looked to the science of mathematics as the supreme tool of natural science.

II

The *Account of the Great Experiment* is by no means Pascal's only treatise on air pressure and hydrostatics. It is preceded, in time, by the *New Experiments Concerning the Vacuum* (pp. 359-365), and followed by the *Treatises on the Equilibrium of Liquids and on the Weight of the Mass of the Air* (pp. 390-429). The experiment described in the present treatise enabled Pascal to see that in the *New Experiments* he held a false opinion, and to correct it in the subsequent *Treatises*.

In the earlier work, Pascal still adheres to the time-honored formula that "nature abhors a vacuum." He records as his first maxim concerning the vacuum:

> That it is repugnant to all bodies to separate from each other and to admit a vacuum between them; that is, nature abhors a vacuum. (p. 365a)

But Pascal was beginning to be suspicious of this horror that nature was supposed to have, as he tells us in the *Great Experiment*:

> When I published my abridgement under the title: *New experiments concerning the vacuum*, etc., in which I had made use of the maxim on the horror of the vacuum because it was universally accepted and because I did not yet have convincing proofs to the contrary, I continued to feel certain difficulties which made me seriously doubt the truth of that maxim; to clear up these difficulties I thought at that time of the experiment here recorded, which would make it possible for me to know with certainty what I ought to believe. (p. 382a)

In the later *Treatise on the Weight of the Mass of the Air*, Pascal has resolved all his doubts and difficulties, for the second chapter in that work is entitled "That the weight of the mass of the air produces all the effects hitherto attributed to the horror of a vacuum."

What is the difference between these two explanations of the same effect? Maxims like "nature abhors a vacuum" were frequently used by the older physicists. We find a trace of this kind of explanation even in Galileo, though he did not rest content with it. When he was looking for an explanation of natural motion (free fall), Galileo wrote:

... in the investigation of naturally accelerated motion we were led, by hand as it were, in following the habit and custom of nature herself, in all her various other processes, to employ only those means which are most common, simple and easy. (Vol. 28, p. 200b)

This might be rephrased as the following maxim: "Nature brings about her effects in the most common, simple, and easy way."

All such explanations of natural effects employ what Aristotle called "final causes." The final cause of an effect is the reason for which it is brought about, or the end and purpose for the sake of which it is done. An explanation in terms of final causes is, therefore, also called a teleological explanation (from the Greek *telos,* which means end).

If we say, for instance, that the reason why water follows the piston in a suction pump is that if it did not, then a vacuum would be created between the water and the piston, we are giving a teleological explanation. We are saying that the cause of the effect (the water's rising) is nothing but nature's desire to avoid a vacuum. Similarly, when Galileo gives as the reason why his definition of naturally accelerated motion should be accepted that it is the simplest and easiest possible motion, his explanation is teleological. For here the effect—a certain kind of motion—is said to be caused by nature's desire for the simple and easy way.

Arguments from final causes began to be severely attacked from about the year 1600 on. Pascal's reasons for feeling uncomfortable with the principle that "nature abhors a vacuum" indicate some of the objections to final causes in general. A major objection is that purposes and ends ought not to be ascribed to something that is inanimate, such as nature. "To tell you frankly what I think," Pascal writes to M. Perier,

it is hard for me to believe that nature, which is not animate or sensitive, is capable of horror, since the passions presuppose a soul capable of feeling them, and I incline much more to impute all these effects to the weight and pressure of the air ... (p. 383a)

Another objection frequently voiced against final causes is that they encourage us to rest content with our ignorance and simply attribute effects to a "purpose" of nature. "When the weakness of men has been unable to find the true causes," Pascal writes near the end of the *Great Experiment*,

their subtlety has substituted imaginary causes, to which they have given specious names filling the ears and not the mind. Thus it is said that the sympathy and antipathy of natural bodies are efficient causes, responsible for many effects, as if inanimate bodies were capable of sympathy and antipathy; it is the same with antiperistasis and with many other chimerical causes, which but give a vain solace to man's hunger to know hidden truths, and which, far from revealing them, serve only to cover up the ignorance of such inventors and to feed that of their followers. (p. 388b)

One of the most powerful attacks on final causes was launched by a contemporary of Pascal's, Benedict de Spinoza (1632-1677). In the Appendix to Part I of his *Ethics*, Spinoza explains why, in his opinion, men seek after the final causes of things and why he thinks that the search for these causes is not merely useless, but actually harmful. Spinoza begins by saying that it is an axiom

that man is born ignorant of the causes of things, and that he has a desire, of which he is conscious, to seek that which is profitable to him. (Vol. 31, p. 369c-d)

One of the consequences of this is

... that man does everything for an end, namely, for that which is profitable to him, which is what he seeks. Hence it happens that he attempts to discover merely the final causes of that which has happened ... (Vol. 31, p. 369d)

But if everything in nature serves man, there must be some mind that directs it in this fashion.

For having considered them [all things] as means it was impossible to believe that they had created themselves, and so he was obliged to infer from the means which he was in the habit of providing for himself that some ruler or rulers of nature exist, endowed with human liberty, who have taken care of all things for him, and have made all things for his use . . . hence he affirmed that the gods direct everything for his advantage . . . (Vol. 31, p. 370a)

Nevertheless, all this is a snare and delusion.

The attempt, however, to show that nature does nothing in vain (that is to say, nothing which is not profitable to man), seems to end in showing that nature, the gods, and man are alike mad. (Vol. 31, p. 370a-b)

The view that everything in nature has been made for man's benefit is in no way compatible with the facts, "such as storms, earthquakes, diseases." (See p. 370b.) Consequently, men retreated to the position of ignorance:

it was looked upon as indisputable that the judgments of the gods far surpass our comprehension; and this opinion alone would have been sufficient to keep the human race in darkness to all eternity, if mathematics, which does not deal with ends, but with the essences and properties of forms, had not placed before us another rule of truth. In addition to mathematics, other causes also might be assigned, which it is superfluous here to enumerate, tending to make men reflect upon these universal prejudices, and leading them to a true knowledge of things. (Vol. 31, p. 370b-c)

The doctrine of final causes, Spinoza says, encourages man's ignorance of nature. One of the most important devices for freeing us from the tyranny of final causes is mathematics. The truth of this statement may be seen in Pascal's *Great Experiment*. What leads Pascal to overthrow the maxim that "nature abhors a vacuum" is the discovery of a precise mathematical relationship between air pressure and the effects previously ascribed to the horror of the vacuum.

What Pascal substitutes for the traditional explanation in terms of final causes is an explanation in terms of efficient causes. That water rises in pumps is not to be explained by reference to an alleged end—nature's desire to avoid a vacuum. Instead, it is to be explained by the air pressing upon the water when the piston in the pump rises. The great experiment confirms that this is the correct explanation. For if it is air pressure that makes the water (or other liquid) rise, then we must expect that the greater the pressure, the higher the liquid will rise. And, similarly, less air pressure should result in less rise on the part of the liquid. The phenomena reported in the *Great Experiment* confirm these expectations.

III

The experiment which Pascal asked his brother-in-law, M. Perier, to perform may be simply described as that of measuring the barometric pressure at two different altitudes: once at the altitude of the town of Clermont, and a second time at the top of the Puy de Dôme, a mountain 4,806 feet high.

The device employed to measure the barometric pressure was—as it almost always is even nowadays—the height of a column of mercury (that is, quicksilver). Mercury is used because it is both liquid and very heavy. The great weight of mercury makes the column of it that is balanced by air quite manageable. At sea level, air pressure will, on the average, support a column of approximately 30 inches. By contrast, it would take a column of water approximately 32 feet high to counterbalance the air pressure.

The "ordinary experiment" to which Pascal refers on p. 383 is performed in the following manner. A glass tube, closed at one end, is filled completely with mercury. The open end is temporarily closed by means of a finger, or in some other way, and the tube is then inserted with its open (but temporarily closed) end into a dish of mercury. The tube must be more than 30 inches in length. When the tube is placed in the dish of mercury and the finger removed, the level of the mercury in the tube will fall; i.e., some of the mercury will run into the open dish. Not all of

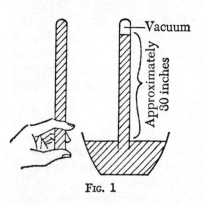

Vacuum

Approximately 30 inches

FIG. 1

the mercury, however, will run out; a column between 29 and 30 inches high will remain in the tube.

Two conclusions are drawn from this experiment. (1) When the mercury level falls after the tube has been inserted into the dish, a vacuum is left at the top of the tube, for the mercury has withdrawn and nothing has rushed in to take its place. This shows that nature does not abhor a vacuum so much that it never permits one to come into existence. It throws grave doubt on the validity of the maxim that "nature *always* abhors a vacuum."

(2) What keeps the mercury in the tube up? It can only be the pressure of the outside air on the dish of mercury. Since the tube is closed at the top, no air presses down on the column of mercury. The mercury in the tube, the mercury in the dish, and a column of air must be imagined to form a system like a U-tube, in which the long column of air balances the short column of mercury.

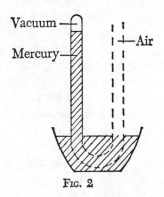

Fig. 2

This experiment was originally performed by Torricelli, who was a student of Galileo's during the last few months of the latter's life. (Pascal describes this experiment on p. 359 in *New Experiments Concerning the Vacuum* and remarks that it was performed in Italy.) It is probable that Galileo urged Torricelli to investigate the so-called horror of the vacuum, for Galileo himself apparently began to have some doubts concerning the validity of this maxim. (You may be interested in Galileo's remarks on the subject in *The Two New Sciences*. They are found in the First Day, on pp. 135c-138a of Volume 28.)

The "great experiment" which M. Perier performed for Pascal consisted of several repetitions of Torricelli's experiment at different altitudes, in order to compare the heights of the mercury columns supported by the air pressure, which becomes progressively less at higher altitudes.

IV

Does the experiment described by M. Perier disprove the existence of nature's horror of a vacuum?

It is perhaps more accurate to say that this "great experiment" deals the finishing blow to the ancient maxim. Torricelli's experiment already showed that nature does not always avoid a vacuum, since a vacuum is created at the top of the tube of mercury. But perhaps it could be maintained that nature had no way of coping with the vacuum created, against its will, at the top of the tube of mercury. Even this attempt at compromise sounds very animistic, imbuing nature with "will" and powers of "coping" with unpleasant situations.

But the experiment on the Puy de Dôme makes the "horror of a vacuum" completely untenable. What reason could be given for saying that nature is less horrified of a vacuum on the top of a mountain than she is at the bottom? And what would be the meaning of a numerically graduated horror? It is interesting to note that it is just the gradual change in the height of the mercury column (according to the elevation at which the experiment is performed) that throws the greatest doubt on the "horror" explanation. Horror seems to be something absolute. An effect that varies in degree, however, seems to call for a cause that varies similarly.

Would Bacon agree with the last statement? How can this notion that cause and effect must co-vary be reconciled with the example of gravity? Gravity, which is a constant force at the surface of the earth, produces a varied effect, namely, different degrees of speed. Or is the variation in speed the function of something that varies?

If there really is a "horror" of the vacuum, so that a vacuum is never permitted to come into existence, then there should be no limit to what nature does to avoid a vacuum. But if the effects formerly ascribed to the horror of the vacuum are really due to the weight of the air, then it cannot surprise us that the effects are proportionate to that weight. In the *Treatise on the Weight of the Air,* Pascal writes:

Since the weight of the air produces all the effects hitherto attributed to the horror of the vacuum, it should be the case that since this weight is not infinite but has limits, its effects too should be limited; which is confirmed by experiment . . . (p. 415b)

Of course, we must add that, strictly speaking, it is impossible to disprove the validity of the ancient maxim. How could one ever prove that there is *not* such a thing as the horror of a vacuum? The nonexistence of something can never be proved. But it can be shown—and Pascal certainly succeeds in showing—that another explanation is so much more plausible that only someone interested in hairsplitting would pay any attention to the logical possibility of the existence of the horror of a vacuum. For example, it is possible that the side of the moon removed from us is made of green cheese. Until someone looks at it or feels it, we cannot completely eliminate that possibility. Nevertheless, no scientist or man of common sense seriously considers the green cheese theory.

What are the precise numerical effects of air pressure in Torricelli's experiment?

In answering this question we are handicapped by the fact that neither Pascal nor M. Perier tells us the elevation at Clermont, nor the precise height of the Puy de Dôme; "about 500 fathoms" is given as the height of the mountain. Furthermore, we do not have precise information on the length of the units which were used to measure either the height of the mountain or the height of the mercury column. "I must tell you," M. Perier writes to Pascal,

that the heights of the quicksilver were very accurately measured; but those of the places where the experiments were performed were much less so.

If I had had the leisure and the facilities, I would have taken the altitudes more precisely, and I would even have marked a place on the mountain for each 100 fathoms of elevation and performed the experiment there and marked the differences found in the height of the quicksilver at each of these stations, in order to give you the exact difference due to the first 100 fathoms, that due to the second 100 fathoms, and similarly of the rest . . . (p. 387b)

However, even given the precise altitudes at which the mercury column is measured, we still cannot rest content, if we are interested in great precision, with simply reading off the height of the mercury in order to determine the air pressure. Even assuming that the altitudes of the locations were measured as precisely as the height of the mercury columns, measurements of the kind M. Perier made can only give approximate results. A change of altitude of 1,000 feet corresponds approximately to a change of 1 inch of mercury, according to M. Perier's figures.

Real precision in measurement, however, requires us to take into account two factors beside elevation, which affect the height of the mercury column. The first is temperature. Mercury expands considerably with heat. Thus it is probable that in M. Perier's experiment the mercury at the top of Puy de Dôme was lower than it would have been, if only the altitude mattered. Undoubtedly, it was colder at the top of the mountain than at the bottom of it.

The second factor is that gravity decreases as we get further away from the center of the earth. Consequently, the column of mercury at over 4,000 feet weighed less than it did at sea level or at the level of the city of Clermont. Hence it took more mercury to balance the column of air there than it would have taken had the mercury been at the level of Clermont.

Actually, even these two things do not exhaust the number of possible sources of error in a barometer. Others affecting the height of the mercury column are the vapor pressure of the mercury and the capillary action of the tube. We merely mention these things to indicate that a simple and beautiful experiment such as this one becomes more and more complicated as scientific knowledge concerning the subject increases. Sometimes it even seems as though the discovery of scientific truths and the performance of crucial experiments depend on the discoverer's *not* knowing a great many things. If he did, and tried to take into account all possible sources of error, he might never have been able to devise his experiment and confirm his theory.

Incidentally, there are still other sources of variation in the height of the mercury column; you might try to think of one.

What is the greatest height to which water can be raised in a suction pump?

This problem is discussed by Galileo. (See Volume 28, pp. 137c-138a.) The answer to the question is that water can be raised to such a height that the weight of a column of it balances the weight of a column of air (of the same diameter). Similarly, of course, mercury can be raised to such a height that *its* weight balances the weight of the corresponding column of air. And since mercury is approximately 13 times as heavy as water, the height to which water can be raised is 13 times greater than that to which mercury can be raised. Numerically, this means that since mercury can be raised to a height of 29 or 30 inches, so water can be raised to about 31 feet. No suction pump will draw water from a greater depth than that.

The following questions are designed to help you test the thoroughness of your reading. Each question is to be answered by giving a page or pages of the reading assignment. Answers will be found on page 224 of this Reading Plan.

1 What did M. Perier use as his "control" in the experiment; that is, how did he satisfy himself that the observed changes in the height of the mercury would not also have taken place if the column of mercury had stayed in the town of Clermont?

2 Was the height of the mercury column affected by the difference of height between the ground level of the cathedral and the top of its tower?

3 How can mercury be employed in an altimeter?

4 Does Pascal think the opinions held in antiquity should be honored or discarded by moderns?

5 How does the great experiment indicate a source of error in thermometers?

6 Was the height of the mercury affected by anything except the altitude at which it was measured?

7 What are the various stages of opinion that Pascal held with respect to the horror of the vacuum?

160

NEWTON

Mathematical Principles of Natural Philosophy

Prefaces, Definitions, Axioms; Book III, Rules, General Scholium

Vol. 34, pp. 1–24, 270–271, 369–372

Occasionally in the history of thought there occurs a moment when some man or some book shatters preceding tradition and advances man's knowledge by a great leap. Such a moment surely occurred with the publication of Newton's *Mathematical Principles*. This is not to say that Newton's work was unprepared for; on the contrary, it represents the culmination of scientific work by such of our authors as Copernicus, Kepler, and Galileo, as well as by many other scientists. In the *Mathematical Principles*, all the previous advances in science become joined together as part of a vast rational system. So comprehensive is Newton's work that it is entirely reasonable for him to entitle the third book of the *Mathematical Principles*, "The System of the World."

Universality is the keynote of this book. Newton undertakes to explain all the phenomena of the world, to subordinate all the physical sciences to his definitions and laws, and finally to reduce everything to "the universal law of gravitation." The moon circling in its orbit and the apple falling from the tree were seen by Newton, according to the familiar fable, to be both manifestations of the same law, that of gravity.

Newton was a fellow and later president of the Royal Society. That society, founded in 1660 for the promotion of experimental natural science, published the *Mathematical Principles* in 1687. It is no exaggeration to say that the Royal Society will be hard pressed to perform a service to mankind as great as that of publishing Newton's masterpiece.

Twelfth Reading

I

Edmund Halley, a friend of Sir Isaac Newton and a famous astronomer (we commemorate his name every time we speak of Halley's Comet) composed an ode to Newton for the first edition of the *Mathematical Principles*. His admiration for Newton is reflected in these concluding lines from the ode:

> Then ye who now on heavenly nectar fare,
> Come celebrate with me in song the name
> Of Newton, to the Muses dear; for he
> Unlocked the hidden treasuries of Truth;
> So richly through his mind had Phoebus cast
> The radiance of his own divinity.
> Nearer the gods no mortal may approach.[1]

To this tribute by an outstanding astronomer let us add the epitaph for Newton composed by the great poet Alexander Pope:

> Nature and Nature's laws lay hid in night;
> God said: "Let Newton be," and all was light.[2]

II

Even in an age as blessed with scientists as was the seventeenth century, Newton's genius was recognized. He became Lucasian Professor of Mathematics at Trinity College in Cambridge in 1669, was elected a fellow of the Royal Society in 1672 (he was its President from 1703 until his death in 1727), was made Warden of the Mint in 1695 and its Master four years later, and was knighted by Queen Anne in 1705.

---

[1] *Mathematical Principles.* Berkeley, California: University of California Press, 1946, p. xv. Translated by Leon J. Richardson.

[2] *Epitaph on Sir Isaac Newton.*

This is not to say that Newton's life was altogether unruffled and untroubled. He was involved in controversy, but most of it was of a scientific nature. Much of it had to do with his theory of light. He first presented his thoughts on this subject to the Royal Society in 1671; his most important papers were collected and published in 1704 in the *Optics*. (Our next reading is taken from this work.) Another dispute arose between him and Leibniz concerning the invention of the infinitesimal calculus.

The *Mathematical Principles,* on which Newton's fame rests securely for all time, was published in 1687. Since the Royal Society was in difficulty about funds at the time, Halley took the whole cost of publication on himself. Concerning this act of generosity and vision, *Encyclopaedia Britannica* properly comments: "We owe much to Halley."

III

The subject matter of the *Mathematical Principles* may be described by a number of phrases, for instance, "experimental physics," "mathematical physics," or "science of nature." Whatever name is used for it, this is a new science, distinctively modern in content and method. Newton still uses the old-fashioned term "natural philosophy" which referred to a branch of learning quite different from what Newton is engaged in; even the title of the work is the *Mathematical Principles of Natural Philosophy*. However, aside from the old-fashioned and inappropriate title which he employs, Newton is quite clear about the new method and aims of his enterprise. He writes:

... I offer this work as the mathematical principles of philosophy [i.e., physics], for the whole burden of philosophy seems to consist in this— from the phenomena of motions to investigate the forces of nature, and then from these forces to demonstrate the other phenomena ... (p. 1b)

After detailing some of his successes in this respect, Newton continues.

I wish we could derive the rest of the phenomena of Nature by the same kind of reasoning from mechanical principles, for I am induced by many reasons to suspect that they may all depend upon certain forces by which the particles of bodies, by some causes hitherto unknown, are either mutually impelled towards one another, and cohere in regular figures, or are repelled and recede from one another. These forces being unknown, philosophers [i.e., physicists] have hitherto attempted the search of Nature in vain; but I hope the principles here laid down will afford some light either to this or some truer method of philosophy. (p. 2a)

Notice the emphasis on "force" in these statements by Newton. "The whole burden" of his science consists in investigating "the forces of nature." In the second statement above, he expresses his conviction that all phenomena are due to the action of forces. It is only ignorance of these forces that has prevented physicists from explaining the observed phenomena and predicting others. The goal of physics, as Newton conceives it, is to find mathematical formulations for the forces that, in his opinion, account for all phenomena.

After this brief summary of Newtonian physics, let us take a look at another kind of physics, often called philosophical physics or philosophy of nature. This is the kind of physics that prevailed prior to 1600; in conception and method, it largely stems from Aristotle. In the first chapter of the work entitled *Physics*, Aristotle tells us what he understands to be the purpose of this discipline.

When the objects of an inquiry, in any department, have principles, conditions, or elements, it is through acquaintance with these that knowledge, that is to say scientific knowledge, is attained. For we do not think that we know a thing until we are acquainted with its primary conditions or first principles, and have carried our analysis as far as its simplest elements. Plainly therefore in the science of Nature, as in other branches of study, our first task will be to try to determine what relates to its principles. (Vol. 8, p. 259a)

There is, therefore, a measure of agreement between Aristotle and Newton. For Newton, we recall, puts the word "principle" into the title of his work. But Newton is looking for mathematical principles. The principles that Aristotle is seeking are quite different. A brief look at the table of contents of the *Physics* will give us an indication of what sort of principles Aristotle has in mind.

Aristotle begins by attempting to discover the number and character of the first principles of everything natural. Then he turns to the conditions of change, discusses the four kinds of causes and the question whether chance is a cause. Next comes the subject of motion, especially the kinds of motion. This in turn leads to discussions of the infinite, of place, of void (vacuum), and of time.

Many of these subjects are of no interest whatever to Newton. For instance, it does not occur to him to ask how many kinds of motion there are. He is interested only in one kind of motion—locomotion—and probably does not think that there are any other kinds. Nor is Newton interested in distinguishing between formal, final, efficient, and material causes. Such problems find no room in the *Mathematical Principles*.

However, some of the topics which Aristotle discusses are also treated by Newton. This is the case with the concepts of space and time. Here, though the subjects treated are the same, the method of treatment is quite different. Aristotle's discussion is conducted from the philosopher's point of view. Newton, as we shall see in the next section, treats space and time from the physicist's point of view.

The distinction between Newton's experimental and mathematical physics, on the one hand, and Aristotle's philosophical physics, on the other, comes down to what the words indicate: Newton is an experimental and mathematical physicist; Aristotle is a philosopher. This difference is reflected in their methods. Newton everywhere uses mathematics and mathematical reasoning; he refers to experiments and observations that bear out his mathematical proofs. Aristotle employs no mathematics whatever, nor does he give any indication of experiments performed. Instead, his method is philosophical; he analyzes, discusses, investigates the consequences of different positions. Neither writer feels any lack in his method. Aristotle does not apologize for the absence of mathematical formulations, nor Newton for the absence of philosophical discussions.

We have already discussed the method of mathematical physics in connection with the Galileo reading. The same remarks apply here, except that Newton presents, perhaps, an even better example of the method. The general pattern is to begin by setting forth certain formulations that explain the phenomena. These are then mathematically demonstrated.

Finally, reference is made to experiments which verify these formulations.

It is important to Newton that in this method no hypotheses are employed. In a famous statement, taken from the General Scholium at the end of the *Mathematical Principles,* he writes:

Hitherto we have explained the phenomena of the heavens and of our sea by the power of gravity, but have not yet assigned the cause of this power. (p. 371b)

He then adds what he knows about the properties of gravity (for instance, that it varies inversely as the square of the distance from its source), and continues as follows:

But hitherto I have not been able to discover the cause of those properties of gravity from phenomena, and I frame no hypotheses; for whatever is not deduced from the phenomena is to be called an hypothesis; and hypotheses, whether metaphysical or physical, whether of occult qualities or mechanical, have no place in experimental philosophy. In this philosophy particular propositions are inferred from the phenomena, and afterwards rendered general by induction. Thus it was that the impenetrability, the mobility, and the impulsive force of bodies, and the laws of motion and gravitation, were discovered. And to us it is enough that gravity does really exist, and act according to the laws which we have explained, and abundantly serves to account for all the motions of the celestial bodies, and of our sea. (pp. 371b-372a)

Are we to take Newton quite literally when he says "I frame no hypotheses?" In the guide to the Galileo reading, we said that the method of mathematical physics consists in making mathematical deductions from hypotheses and verifying these results. Is not Newton's method the same? Does he not, too, use hypotheses? It seems to be so. In Book I, for instance, Newton begins to investigate what happens to bodies that move under the influence of an attractive force that is inversely proportional to the square of the distance from a point. Using this hypothesis, it follows that a body moves in an ellipse around the center of force. Thus Newton's method fits into the pattern of (1) hypothesis, namely, that the force emanating from the sun obeys an inverse square law, (2) mathematical deduction, namely, that the path of a body in an inverse square field is an ellipse, and (3) verification, namely, that the planets do in fact move in ellipses about the sun.

In what sense, then, does Newton *not* make hypotheses?

The answer probably lies in two different meanings of the term "hypothesis."

In the sense of a tentative formulation—to be explored mathematically and verified or disproved by experiment— Newton does make hypotheses. But there is a second meaning of hypothesis. In this sense, a hypothesis is something fictional, an invention, a figment of the imagination. An example of this kind of hypothesis might be nature's horror of a vacuum. A better instance is any attempt to offer an "occult" quality as the explanation for a phenomenon. Thus, if it is said that fire heats bodies because of its calorific tendency, the phrase "calorific tendency" exemplifies the kind of hypothesis that Newton despises and refuses to make. No explanation is provided by this sort of hypothesis; nor is it in any sense testable by experiment. In fact, to say that bodies which heat other bodies are calorific is merely to repeat the description of the phenomenon, not to explain it. "Calorific," after all, means "heat-making."

Even to say that bodies fall because of gravity is dangerously close to an explanation by an occult quality. "Gravity" means heaviness; we appear to be saying that heavy bodies fall because of heaviness. Newton avoids this, because he does not rest content to explain fall simply by the term "gravity." He finds out what causes it (the mass of bodies), how large it is (inversely proportional to the square of the distance from its source), and what its precise effects are (motion in an ellipse or other conic section). Thus, he does not treat gravity as an occult quality or fictitious hypothesis, but as something that can be measured, subjected to mathematical treatment, and whose effects can be subjected to experimental verification.

IV

Just as in the last section we discussed the characteristics of the Newtonian method, so in this section we shall discuss some of the characteristic concepts of Newtonian physics. These concepts are discussed at the beginning of the *Mathematical Principles,* in the sections entitled "Definitions" and "Axioms, or Laws of Motion."

(a) One of Newton's basic concepts is that of inertia. He discusses it in Definition III, and again in Law I. It is an innate force of matter "by which every body, as much as in it lies, continues in its present state, whether it be of rest, or of moving uniformly forwards in a right [straight] line." (See p. 5b.) Every body, this tells us, has a tendency to remain in the state in which it is. This is easy to accept for a body which is in the state of rest. What Newton adds here, however, is that if a body is in a state of uniform straight motion, then it will also have a tendency to stay in that state. This is a new idea. Aristotle, for instance, thought that a body in motion always required a propulsive force in order to keep it going. Without force, there is no motion, in the Aristotelian scheme.

Bodies are seen to behave differently in the Newtonian scheme. "As much as in it lies," a body stays in motion if it is in uniform motion. Law I then tells us what it takes to disturb a body from its inertial state. An impressed force is required.

Every body continues in its state of rest, or of uniform motion in a right line, unless it is compelled to change that state by forces impressed upon it. (p. 14a)

In the Newtonian scheme, therefore, without force, there is no non-inertial motion, but there well may be inertial motion.

Everyday experience confirms that there is such a thing as inertia. We all know that bodies are only changed with difficulty from rest to motion; for example, it takes a great deal more strength to get a car to roll by pushing than it takes to keep it rolling once it has begun to move. Inertia tends to keep the car at rest, just as inertia tends to keep it moving once it has begun to move. Inertia is similarly responsible for making a passenger in an automobile lean to the left when the car turns right. The body in question, namely, the passenger, has a tendency to keep going in a straight line. Hence if the car turns to the right, he keeps going straight, which, relative to the moving car, manifests itself as leaning to the left.

This principle of inertia is not something completely new and invented by Newton. There are clear indications in Galileo's work that he was aware of it. For instance, in the Third

Day (somewhat farther on than the portion which we have read), Galileo writes:

Furthermore, we may remark that any velocity once imparted to a moving body will be rigidly maintained as long as the external causes of acceleration or retardation are removed, a condition which is found only on horizontal planes; for in the case of planes which slope downwards there is already present a cause of acceleration, while on planes sloping upward there is retardation; from this it follows that motion along a horizontal plane is perpetual; for, if the velocity be uniform, it cannot be diminished or slackened, much less destroyed. (Vol. 28, p. 224d)

What, then, does Newton contribute over and beyond Galileo's recognition that uniform straight-line motion is inertial? Newton sees things in a larger context than Galileo. He recognizes that all uniform straight-line motion is inertial, not only motion on a horizontal plane. He recognizes that rest and uniform straight-line motion are two manifestations of the same thing. And, finally, he recognizes what it takes to disturb a body out of its inertial condition, namely, force.

(b) Of the three Laws of Motion, the third one is perhaps the most important. It is also the law which is Newton's own discovery. We have already seen how Galileo anticipated the First Law (the law of inertia); evidence can be found that Galileo also partially anticipated the Second Law. No one before Newton, however, thought of the Third Law:

To every action there is always opposed an equal reaction: or, the mutual actions of two bodies upon each other are always equal, and directed to contrary parts. (p. 14b)

This law always seems puzzling on a first reading. No real difficulty remains, however, if we clearly understand, in any situation, which body is acting and which body is acted on. Suppose I tie a string around a rock and pull it toward me. The pull constitutes force. How does Newton's Third Law hold true here? What is the action and what is the reaction?

The action is *my pulling the rock.* In this action, I am the agent and the rock is the patient. That is to say, I am doing something to the rock, namely pulling it.

The reaction is the *rock's pulling me.* In this reaction, the rock is the agent and I am the patient. That is to say, the rock is doing something to me, namely, pulling me. How do we know that there is really such a reaction? Take a look at the string while I am pulling the rock. It is taut. This is due to the fact that while I am pulling the rock one way, the rock is pulling me the other way. The result: a string which is taut because it is being pulled in both directions. If there were no reaction, if there were only pull in one way, the string and rock would simply come toward me, without being taut.

The important thing to realize with respect to action and reaction is that they are two forces impressed on two different bodies. If they were impressed upon the same body, they would, of course, cancel one another out and there would be no motion. This is how it often seems to someone upon first reading the Third Law. This difficulty is obviated once it is realized that the two forces act on two different bodies—the rock acts on me, while I act on the rock.

Another example may be helpful. Imagine a person in a rowboat, near the dock. (The only reason for using a boat in the example is that friction is minimized here.) Now let the person in the boat push against the dock with an oar. What happens? The boat with the person in it will recede from the dock. Here the action is the person's pushing of the dock. This action probably has no visible results, because the dock is securely anchored against the shore. The reaction is the dock's pushing the person and the boat in which he is. The result: the motion of the person and boat away from the dock.

Actually all vehicles rely on the Third Law to move forward. In a car, the wheels push against the pavement, while the pavement pushes against the wheels and so makes the car go forward. In walking, the feet push against the ground, which responds by pushing against the feet and so moving them. In an airplane, the propeller moves and pushes back the air; consequently, the air pushes the propeller in the opposite direction; i.e., forward. In a rocket, the engine sends a blast of vapors backward; consequently, the vapors push the rocket forward. These examples should suffice to show that there is probably no more universally applicable law than this one.

(c) A third new idea which Newton introduced into the

science of dynamics is that time and space are absolute as well as relative quantities. What space and time are seems to him clear, but the distinction between absolute and relative space as applied to space and time stands in need of explanation.

> I do not define time, space, place, and motion, as being well known to all. Only I must observe, that the common people conceive those quantities under no other notions but from the relation they bear to sensible objects. And thence arise certain prejudices, for the removing of which it will be convenient to distinguish them into absolute and relative, true and apparent, mathematical and common. (p. 8b)

Let us note how he defines absolute time and absolute space:

> Absolute, true, and mathematical time, of itself, and from its own nature, flows equably without relation to anything external, and by another name is called duration . . .
>
> Absolute space, in its own nature, without relation to anything external, remains always similar and immovable. (p. 8b)

What does Newton mean by the concepts of absolute time and absolute space? In each case, Newton emphasizes independence from anything external, sameness, uniformity, and ability to exist by itself. Absolute time is said to "flow equably," while absolute space "remains always similar and immovable."

It should be clear that there is something strange in the notion of time as something absolute, as existing independently of motion. Aristotle calls time "number of movement in respect of the before and after." (See *Physics*, Bk. IV, Ch. 11, Vol. 8, p. 300a.) Time is, of course, measured by uniform motions, either those of a clock or else the motions of the sun or fixed stars. In these cases, therefore, time is considered as an attribute or quality of motion, not as a self-subsisting thing. Time, in Aristotle's view and also in the view implied by the use of measuring instruments, does not exist by itself but only with and in a motion. Time is always the time of a motion; five minutes is the time that belongs to a certain motion of the hands of a clock, a year is the time that belongs to a complete revolution of the sun.

Newton would dismiss all these examples as merely relative time. Absolute time is for him a thing. It exists. It has qualities, rather than being a quality. It flows uniformly forever, though Newton does not tell us within what it flows.

Absolute space is also a subsisting thing. As absolute time flows uniformly and eternally, so absolute space extends infinitely in all directions. No part of it is distinguishable from any other. Thus absolute space is not associated with any body or bodies. It is something independent of body and void. It is pure dimensionality.

V

How does Newton describe his method of reasoning?

Newton rejects any reasoning not based on experiment and induction. At the beginning of Book III, in a section entitled "Rules of Reasoning in Philosophy," Newton tells us what logical principles he employs. They are four in number and we can sum them up as follows:

1. *The rule of simplicity.* No unnecessary causes are to be admitted into "philosophy," but only such as are "both true and sufficient" to explain the phenomena at hand. This rejects final causes, although in giving his reason for this rule, Newton seems to be appealing to something like a final cause. "Nature is pleased with simplicity," he writes, "and affects not the pomp of superfluous causes." In any case, Newton wants to explain phenomena with as few and as simple causes as possible. The requirement that they be "true" is almost surely meant to exclude any fanciful causes, such as nature's horror of a vacuum.

2. *The rule of consilience.* Instead of looking for more and more causes, as we investigate more and more phenomena, we should try to explain new phenomena by old causes. This is not only economical; it also adds to the persuasiveness of a system to have many things explained by few causes. One of the most admired features of Newton's system is that one cause—gravity—explains so many things: the fall of bodies, the revolution of the planets, the action of the tides, and so on. This rule shows that Newton wants to model physics on mathematics. In the Preface, he writes: ". . . it is the glory of geometry that from those few principles, brought from without, it is able to produce so many things." (See p. 1a-b.) Rules

1 and 2 are closely related; they might almost have been combined in one rule.

3. *The rule of empiricism.* This rule tells us to rely on our experience and therefore, on experiments. "We are certainly not," Newton writes, "to relinquish the evidence of experiments for the sake of dreams and vain fictions of our own devising . . ." (See p. 270b.) What he has in mind are "occult qualities," attributed to bodies in order to explain otherwise incomprehensible phenomena. In particular, he probably means to reject an invisible, weightless ether (sometimes used to explain the phenomena of light), or any other quality which is not directly accessible to the senses.

4. *The rule of induction.* Just as Rule 1 and Rule 2 belong closely together, so do Rules 3 and 4. This fourth rule really just reaffirms the principle of empiricism. What we learn from experience and from inductions based on experience, we are to consider as true. No fanciful hypotheses are to be permitted to throw doubt on inductive results, even though it may be true that an induction can never assure perfect certainty for its conclusion. In spite of this fact, we are to go along with induction so that "the argument of induction may not be evaded by hypotheses."

We have earlier commented on Newton's distrust of hypotheses. But we also pointed out that, in one sense of the term "hypothesis," he does use them. The mathematical formulations with which the *Mathematical Principles* are filled constitute hypotheses, we said. They or their consequences (arrived at by mathematical deduction) are verified by experiments and observation. But nowhere in the Rules does Newton mention such tentative formulations. He speaks as though all his results came from induction.

Is Newton correct in the description of his method or does he ignore the role of hypotheses? For instance, how do you suppose Newton arrived at the proposition that the sun attracts the planets with a force inversely proportional to the square of their distances from the sun? Is this an inductive conclusion, resulting from many observations of the sun and the planets? Or is it a hypothesis, later verified because one of its consequences (that the planets move in ellipses about the sun) is found to be true?

Does Newton continue the "Keplerian revolution"?

We used the phrase "Keplerian revolution" to signify Kepler's abandonment of the view that terrestrial and celestial phenomena had to be treated differently. Newton certainly agrees with Kepler and, in fact, carries his point of view even further. All matter, says Newton, is of one kind; and all matter has one and the same property: gravity. Newton tells us this in his celebrated law of universal gravitation, which is stated as Proposition 7 of Book III of the *Mathematical Principles*. "There is," he writes, "a power of gravity pertaining to all bodies, proportional to the several quantities of matter which they contain." (See p. 281b.) Consequently, all phenomena are to be explained in the same way: as the result of gravity.

In what sense does this explanation go beyond Kepler's view of the relation of celestial and terrestrial phenomena? Is the law of universal gravitation the result of induction? Does Bacon's method of induction have any relevance to Newton's work?

How does Newton distinguish between absolute and relative motion?

The problem is to find a way of knowing whether body A is really (i.e., absolutely) in motion, or whether it only seems to be in motion relative to some other body B. Or, if A has some absolute motion as well as some motion relative to B, we seek a way of separating the absolute from the relative motion.

The problem would be easily solved, if we as observers could somehow look down from absolute space upon bodies A and B. Then, any motion of A relative to absolute space would be its absolute motion. But, of course, we cannot do that; we are not bodiless, suspended in absolute space. We are bodies, on the earth, and so have to take into account that the motions we observe may be relative to a motion of our own, or relative to the motion of the earth.

Body A may be in motion relative to B, even though no force is acting on A. It suffices that somehow or other B moves. B's motion means that A has relative motion (namely, relative to B).

But if some force acts on A, then A must really move, not just relative to B.

The causes by which true and relative motions are distinguished, one from the other, are the forces impressed upon bodies to generate motion. True motion is neither generated nor altered, but by some force impressed upon the body moved; but relative motion may be generated or altered without any force impressed upon the body. (p. 11a)

Similarly, whenever we know that a body is moving non-inertially, we know that its motion is caused by a force and so is an absolute motion. If a body is rotating, we can tell whether its motion is merely relative or absolute, by discovering whether a force is present.

The effects which distinguish absolute from relative motion are, the forces of receding from the axis of circular motion. For there are no such forces in a circular motion purely relative, but in a true and absolute circular motion, they are greater or less, according to the quantity of the motion. (p. 11b)

Is there any way of telling whether straight-line motion is absolute or relative? What is the point of wanting to know whether a given motion is relative or absolute?

The following questions are designed to help you test the thoroughness of your reading. Each question is to be answered by giving a page or pages of the reading assignment. Answers will be found on page 224 of this Reading Plan.

1 Is there necessarily some truly uniform motion whereby absolute time can be measured?

2 How does Newton find the motion of a body that is acted on simultaneously by two forces?

3 Does Newton think it is possible for a man-made satellite to revolve in an orbit around the earth?

4 How does Newton generalize Archimedes' Law of the Lever?

5 Suppose there were only two bodies in the world, and that these two bodies, by acting on one another, describe ellipses about each other. What would the common center of gravity of these two bodies be doing?

6 Is the consideration of God and his attributes a proper part of natural philosophy?

7 What are the qualities that Newton enumerates as the universal qualities of all bodies?

8 What is the general principle according to which simple machines, like the lever or inclined plane, operate?

NEWTON

Optics

Book I, Part I, Definitions, Axioms, Prop. 1–2

Book III, Part I, Queries 27–31

Vol. 34, pp. 379–404, 525–544

It is our common world that men of science inquire into. The world is here for all of us, but most of us accept it unquestioningly. The scientist seeks for underlying patterns that will account for the events and conditions of ordinary experience. You may have been struck by the simplicity of the phenomena that have attracted the attention of the powerful scientific minds we have been studying—floating bodies, falling bodies, air pressure.

In this reading, Newton is concerned with ordinary light. This is the light by which we do our work and enjoy the beauties of nature and art. We take it for granted, but Newton inquires about it. What is its constitution? What laws does it obey? How are white light and colored light related? Why are there optical illusions? How do eyeglasses improve vision?

Newton's method in this book is strictly experimental. He renders no mere lip service to the experimental creed of modern science. You have only to read his description of an experiment to be assured of this. You will be impressed by his meticulous attention to detail. ("In the Sun's light let into my darkened chamber through a small round hole in my window-shut, at about ten or twelve feet from the window, I placed a lens . . .")

Optics was a subject of life-long interest to Newton. Though the *Optics* was published 17 years after the *Mathematical Principles,* some of the observations were made 15 years prior to the latter's publication. In the *Mathematical Principles,* Newton's aim is grand and universal and his method is mathematical. In the *Optics,* he is concerned with details and minute observation; his method is experimental. The mind of Newton could accommodate itself to both perspectives.

Thirteenth Reading

I

With the exception of Euclid's *Elements* and Nicomachus' *Introduction to Arithmetic,* none of our selections has been from works of pure mathematics. Most of the books we have read have been in the field of natural science. Nevertheless, many of these works, though not pure mathematics, adhere very closely to forms obviously derived from Euclid. These books are arranged like the *Elements:* they begin with definitions, axioms, and postulates, and then proceed to a series of propositions.

The *Mathematical Principles* and the *Optics* both follow the Euclidean pattern. Nevertheless, the two books differ considerably in method, in spite of their superficial similarity in form. We have repeatedly pointed out that the *Mathematical Principles* is a work in mathematical physics. It is characterized mainly by the mathematical development of certain tentative formulations. The role of experiments is rather secondary in this work.

The *Optics,* on the other hand, may be called a work in experimental physics. Its characteristic is that general principles are developed by experimentation. Mathematics, though present, has a very minor role here.

Newton describes his method in the next to last paragraph of the *Optics,* as follows:

As in mathematics, so in natural philosophy, the investigation of difficult things by the method of analysis, ought ever to precede the method of composition. This analysis consists in making experiments and observations, and in drawing general conclusions from them by induction, and admitting of no objections against the conclusions but such as are taken from experiments, or other certain truths. For hypotheses are not to be regarded in experimental philosophy. And although the arguing from experiments and observations by induction be no demonstration of general conclusions, yet it is the best way of arguing which the nature of things admits of, and may be looked upon as so much the stronger, by how much the induction is more general. And if no exception occur from phenomena, the conclusion may be pronounced generally. But if at any time afterwards any exception shall occur from experiments, it may then begin to be pronounced with such exceptions as occur. By this way of analysis we may proceed from compounds to ingredients, and from motions to the forces producing them; and, in general, from effects to their causes, and from particular causes to more general ones, till the argument end in the most general. This is the method of analysis; and the synthesis consists in assuming the causes discovered, and established as principles, and by them explaining the phenomena proceeding from them, and proving the explanations. (p. 543a-b)

The *Optics* employs the method of analysis; the *Mathematical Principles*, on the other hand, uses the method of synthesis. Notice that Newton does not hesitate to admit the use of hypotheses in the synthetic method. "Synthesis consists in *assuming* the causes discovered" (italics added); for instance, the existence of an inverse square force emanating from the sun is assumed and the phenomena, such as the planetary paths, are explained by means of this assumption.

Before the synthetic method can be used, the causes (such as the inverse square force) must have been discovered. It is the business of analysis to make these discoveries. That is why Newton writes that "the investigation of difficult things by the method of analysis ought ever to precede the method of composition." Synthesis can only be used in a well-developed and far advanced science; in fields where research and investigation are just beginning, analysis is called for.

Optics, in Newton's time, was a field in which not much previous work had been done. Kepler had written a book on optics, and knew the law of reflection. The law of refraction had been discovered by Snell in 1621. These two laws constituted almost all that was known in optics. Newton summarizes these laws and a few additional things in the axioms. At the end of the section dealing with axioms he writes:

I have now given in Axioms and their explications the sum of what hath hitherto been treated of in Optics. For what hath been generally agreed on I content myself to assume under the notion of Principles, in order to what I have further to write. (p. 386b)

We can see from this that the similarity between Euclid's *Elements,* the *Mathematical Principles,* and the *Optics* is merely superficial. Although each of these three books employs axioms, they by no means are the same thing in all three. In the *Elements,* the axioms state self-evident truths that are universally applicable. In the *Mathematical Principles,* the axioms state the very general Laws of Motion, which form the basis of the entire science of dynamics. In the *Optics,* the axioms merely state what was generally accepted in that science around the year 1700.

In the matter of its propositions, the *Optics* also differs from the *Mathematical Principles* and the *Elements.* In the latter two works, the propositions are rigorously demonstrated by means of axioms and propositions previously proved. Such procedure is typical of the synthetic method, where principles of the highest generality (such as Euclid's postulates, or Newton's axioms) are assumed at the beginning for the purpose of developing their consequences by deductive reasoning.

In contrast, in the *Optics* the propositions do not state conclusions that are to be demonstrated from general principles. Rather, the propositions state principles that have been found as the result of analysis and induction. The proofs of the propositions are, therefore, not mathematical demonstrations. They are accounts of the experimental and inductive methods employed to arrive at the generalizations that are stated in the propositions. Indeed, after the statement of each proposition, Newton places the phrase, "The Proof by Experiment." This very accurately describes the method. The crucial part of each proof is the experiment, or series of experiments, that Newton devises in order to give plausibility to his proposition. From the experiments, the proposition in question is then inferrable by induction. Thus the *Optics* follows the rule laid down in the *Mathematical Principles:*

In experimental philosophy we are to look upon propositions inferred by general induction from phenomena as accurately or very nearly true, not-

*withstanding any contrary hypotheses that may be imagined, till such
time as other phenomena occur, by which they may either be made more
accurate, or liable to exceptions.* (p. 271b)

II

The axioms state the basic laws of optics: (1) In reflection,
the angle of incidence is equal to the angle of reflection. (2) In
refraction, the sine of the angle of incidence is to the sine of
the angle of refraction in a given (i.e., fixed) ratio. Let us examine these two laws.

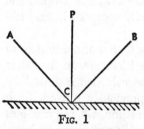

Fig. 1

(1) Suppose a ray AC falls upon
a reflecting surface (a surface
which does not let the ray of light
penetrate, but returns it) at the
point C. (See Fig. 1.) Then the
angle of incidence is the angle
which ray AC makes with the perpendicular at the point of incidence. Hence, if we draw this
perpendicular, CP, and then draw CB so that the angle BCP
is equal to the angle ACP, we shall have found the reflected
ray.

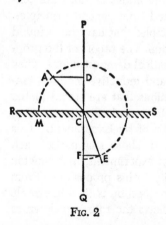

Fig. 2

(2) In order to understand the
law of refraction (Axiom V, often
called Snell's Law, after its discoverer), let us again draw a ray
AC incident at C upon a refracting medium (i.e., a medium such
as water which permits the
light to travel through it). Strictly
speaking, of course, the ray AC
also travels through a refracting
medium, namely air. The line RS,
therefore, is the border of two refracting media. Of the two, water
is the denser medium. Axiom IV
tells us, first of all, that the ray AC in traveling from air into
water will be bent toward the perpendicular. Axiom V tells us

just how much the ray AC will be deflected when it penetrates into the water. No matter what the angle of incidence of AC, it will be refracted into a ray CE (see Fig. 2) such that the sine of angle ACP is to the sine of angle ECQ as 4 is to 3. The sines in question are, as Newton points out, the perpendiculars AD and EF, where A and E are both on a circle drawn with C as the center. The ratio 4:3 is the "given" ratio that Newton mentions in the statement of the axiom. It is also called the index of refraction and varies from medium to medium. If the refraction is from air into glass, the index is 17:11. If the refraction is from water into air it is, of course, 3:4, just as the index of refraction from glass into air is 11:17.

The law of refraction may be expressed by saying that the index of refraction of light going from one medium to another depends only on the physical constitution of the two media. What Newton does in Proposition 1 is to add the qualification that this holds true only for homogeneal or simple light; i.e., light all of the same color. For light rays of different colors, the index of refraction depends also on the color. Blue light is refracted much more sharply than red light; the other colors of the rainbow fall between these two in refrangibility. The experiments which prove this (remember that Newton explicitly calls them "proofs by experiment") are quite simple and yet very persuasive.

In Proposition 1, Newton obtains his blue and his red light by looking through a prism at a piece of paper that is partially colored a deep blue and partially a deep red. The rays of light that come from the blue part of the paper are blue, while the rays that come to the eye from the red portion of the paper are red. Although he is looking at one piece of paper, the blue part of the paper seems considerably higher than the red part. This is explained by the greater refrangibility of the blue light as compared with the red light.

From this beginning Newton goes on to several other discoveries, all of them concerned with colors and colored light. For instance, in Proposition 2 he shows that the light of the sun can be divided into rays of different colors. Later on, Newton explains how the fact that the sun's (white) light is really

a mixture of colored light accounts for the imperfection of refracting telescopes. He also gives an explanation of the rainbow, advances a theory to explain the colors of bodies, and
shows that light consisting of the seven colors of the rainbow
can again be mixed to produce white light.

III

In addition to making many experimental discoveries concerning colors and colored light, Newton also made a contribution to the general theory of the nature of light: not in the
Optics, however, which is largely a work in experimental
physics, but in the *Mathematical Principles* where the theory
of refraction is developed. In Book I, Section XIV of that work
(pp. 152-157), Newton investigates what happens to small
bodies when they are attracted continuously to a plane that
separates two media. Newton finds that he can derive Snell's
Law, provided he makes these assumptions: (1) that light
consists of very small bodies, i.e., corpuscles; (2) that refraction is caused by a force of attraction exerted on these light
corpuscles in a direction perpendicular to the plane between
the two media and depending in amount only on the distance
from that separating plane.

In the Scholium on page 155a of Volume 34, Newton writes:
"These attractions bear a great resemblance to the reflections
and refractions of light made in a given ratio of the secants, as
was discovered by Snell . . ." And at the end of the Scholium,
he adds:

Therefore because of the analogy there is between the propagation of the
rays of light and the motion of bodies, I thought it not amiss to add the
following Propositions for optical uses; not at all considering the nature
of the rays of light, or inquiring whether they are bodies or not; but only
determining the curves of bodies which are extremely like the curves of
the rays. (p. 155b)

To suppose that light consists of corpuscles does not seem
like a bad assumption. Common sense can quite readily accept
the picture that a ray of light consists of tiny bodies that travel
in a steady stream.

In Query 29 of Book III of the *Optics*, Newton mentions the corpuscular theory of light.

Are not the rays of light very small bodies emitted from shining substances? For such bodies will pass through uniform mediums in right lines without bending into the shadow, which is the nature of the rays of light. (p. 529b)

Newton describes light as always traveling in a straight line, without bending into the shadow of an obstruction. This characteristic of light is easily explained by the corpuscular theory, but it gives some difficulty to its great rival, the wave theory of light. We shall encounter the wave theory in the next reading and there discuss, in some detail, the point about light not bending into the shadow.

Whether or not light does in fact consist of corpuscles is one of the famous disputes in physics.

One consequence of the corpuscular theory of light is that light travels more swiftly in a denser than in a rarer medium. (See *Mathematical Principles*, Book I, Prop. 95, p. 154a.) It follows from the wave theory, however, that light travels more rapidly in a rarer medium than in a denser one. The two theories, therefore, make different predictions about a phenomenon (the speed of light) which at the time of Newton had never been observed. The Newtonian corpuscular theory predicts that light travels more swiftly in water than in air; the wave theory predicts that light travels more swiftly in air than in water

Here is an opportunity for a truly crucial experiment. All we need to do is measure the speed of light in water and in air and see which is greater in order to decide between the theories. If light travels more swiftly in air than in water, the wave theory must be correct; if light travels more swiftly in water than in air, the corpuscular theory must be right.

This crucial experiment was performed by Foucault in 1850. He measured the speed of light in air and water and found that the speed in air is greater. This experiment, therefore, decisively confirmed the wave theory and apparently dealt a death blow to the corpuscular theory.

Nature, however, is less neat than we would like it to be. Since 1850, additional phenomena have been discovered which cannot be reconciled with the wave theory of light. The exact nature of light and whether it is undular or corpuscular in character is, therefore, still somewhat in doubt.

IV

What is the method employed by Newton to prove the axioms in the Optics?

No proof at all is offered for the axioms. If these were axioms in Euclid's sense, namely self-evident truths, there would, of course, be no need for proofs. The axioms in the *Optics,* however, are not self-evident; they merely state "what hath been generally agreed on." Such general agreement also makes proof unnecessary, until someone comes along who fails to agree that the matters stated are true. How could such a person be convinced?

It is actually quite easy to show that the law of reflection and the law of refraction are true. One or two experiments will show that a light ray does in fact travel as these laws say it does. The laws of reflection and refraction are easily verifiable because they are nothing but empirical generalizations. They do not explain why the phenomena happen as they do; they merely describe how they happen. An explanation of why reflection and refraction behave as they do would have to come from a general theory of light. Both the corpuscular and the undular theories offer such explanations.

The axioms tell us which path a light ray follows after reflection or refraction. A light ray may be represented by a line and the laws of reflection and refraction tell how to draw the lines after the light ray has hit a reflecting or refracting surface. This way of dealing with light and light rays is often called *geometrical optics.* A causal explanation of reflection or refraction in terms of corpuscles or waves would, by contrast, be a part of *physical optics.*

Should geometrical optics be classified as a part of mathematical physics? Or does it belong to experimental physics?

Have we encountered any other instances of a science in which physical things are treated like mathematical entities, without any regard to their physical qualities? Would you say that Archimedes' treatment of the Law of the Lever was an instance of "geometrical mechanics"?

Is this way of treating physical things related to the way in which ancient astronomers treated the heavenly bodies? Is Ptolemy's treatment of astronomical problems geometrical or physical? Is it descriptive or causal?

How does the law of refraction explain the bent appearance of a stick submerged in water?

The light rays coming from the part of the stick under water are bent as they emerge from the water, while the light rays coming from the part of the stick above the water are not bent. Figure 3 will help to explain. Let the stick be ABC, with B the point at which it enters the water's surface. Let the eye of the observer be placed at E. Then a ray of light starting from the end C of the stick will be refracted at the point D and travel to the eye along the line DE. The eye, therefore, will assume that the end C of the stick is along the line DE, at the point F. Rays starting from other points of the submerged part of the stick will be bent similarly. The stick, therefore, will seem to be in the position FBA, when seen from E. Newton explains in Axiom VIII why the point C will seem to be at F: *"An object seen by reflexion or refraction appears in that place from whence the rays after their last reflexion or refraction diverge in falling on the spectator's eye."* (See p. 385b.)

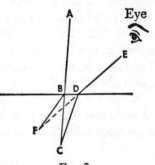

Fig. 3

Are there any practical consequences of the different
refrangibility of light rays of different color?

Rainbows are pretty, but for the most part the dispersion of
white light is troublesome. Since blue light is refracted more
than red light, it follows that white light cannot be focused
perfectly with a lens. Since the
blue light bends more than the
red light, the light that eman-
ates from one point in front
of the lens will be focused in
two or more places behind the
lens. This is especially trouble-
some in the case of telescopes. Thus Newton tells us in Proposition 7 of Book I, Part I, that "the perfection of telescopes is
impeded by the different refrangibility of the rays of light."
He tried to overcome this imperfection, but failed and con-
cluded that "the improvement of telescopes of given lengths
by refractions is desperate." (See p. 420b.) Hence he turned to
building a telescope which employed the principles of reflection rather than those of refraction.

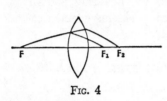

Fig. 4

Newton was wrong in his statement that the improvement
of refracting telescopes is desperate. It is possible to construct
a so-called achromatic lens, that is, a lens which refracts without dispersion. This is possible
because different kinds of glass
have different refractive powers.
By a suitable choice of materials
and of the shapes of the lenses,
it is possible to combine two
lenses so that the greater refraction of red light in one lens is
canceled out by the lesser refraction of it in the other lens.

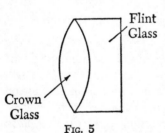

Flint
Glass

Crown
Glass

Fig. 5

Such an achromatic lens looks approximately like the one in
the accompanying diagram. Most so-called achromatic lenses
are not perfectly achromatic, but manage at least to bring the
red and blue light rays together in one place.

The following questions are designed to help you test the thoroughness of your reading. Each question is to be answered by giving a page or pages of the reading assignment. Answers will be found on page 224 of this Reading Plan.

1 What is Newton's definition of a ray of light?

2 What is the cause of farsightedness and nearsightedness in men?

3 What does Newton conceive to be God's role in creation?

4 Does Newton think that the world was created by God or simply arose out of chaos?

5 What is refrangibility?

6 Does anything affect refrangibility of homogeneal light except its color?

7 If both red light and blue light, emanating from the same point, are focused by a lens, which image will be closer to the lens?

191

HUYGENS

Treatise on Light

Preface, Ch. I–IV

Vol. 34, pp. 551–578

Sometimes in the history of human achievement, one man's true greatness overshadows another's true greatness. Such was the case in the 17th century when Sir Isaac Newton towered like a colossus over all his brilliant contemporaries. There was another great scientific genius in 17th-century science who deserves equal credit with Newton for establishing a scientific theory of light—Christiaan Huygens. Indeed, Huygens' wave theory won acceptance over Newton's corpuscular theory during the 19th century. Only then did the science of optics fully recognize its debt to this great Dutchman.

Huygens continues the development of modern science along the lines that we have observed in the works of Galileo and Newton. Like them, he is a brilliant mathematician. Like them, his interests cover almost all of physical science. Like them, he achieved fame in his lifetime, received many honors, and corresponded with all his famous learned contemporaries.

Huygens writes of his subject and his purposes in a direct, human way that is a far cry from the arid pages of a textbook. Listen to him:

I would believe then that those who love to know the causes of things and who are able to admire the marvels of light, will find some satisfaction in these various speculations regarding it, and in the new explanation of its famous property which is the main foundation of the construction of our eyes, and of those great inventions which extend so vastly the use of them.

Here you have Huygens' genial invitation to the present reading.

I

Christiaan Huygens' life and period of major activity slightly precede and overlap Newton's. Huygens was born in 1629 and died in 1695; Newton lived from 1642 to 1727. Huygens' greatest work, the *Horologium oscillatorium,* which deals with the pendulum clock, was published in 1673, and the *Treatise on Light,* written in 1678, was published in 1690. Newton's *Mathematical Principles* was published in 1687, and the *Optics* was not published until 1704, although most of the important parts of it were communicated to the Royal Society between 1672 and 1678. Huygens was elected a fellow of the Royal Society in 1663, while Newton became a fellow of the society in 1672.

Huygens tells us in the Preface to the *Treatise on Light* that he wrote it while he lived in France and that he first presented it in 1678 to the French Royal Academy of Science, "to the membership of which the King [Louis XIV] had done me the honour of calling me." This accounts for the fact that the *Treatise* is written in French. Huygens intended to translate the book into Latin later on, but, he tells us,

... the pleasure of novelty being past, I have put off from time to time the execution of this design, and I know not when I shall ever come to an end of it, being often turned aside either by business or by some new study. (p. 551b)

The use of a vernacular language for a learned treatise became acceptable only in modern times. Before 1600, anything but Latin would have been unthinkable. Scientific treatises were the first scholarly works to be written in the everyday languages. Descartes, though he first published his *Discourse on Method* in French, nevertheless had it translated into Latin.

Spinoza's *Ethics* was written in Latin and not translated in his lifetime. However, Descartes' *Geometry* was written in French, Galileo's *Two New Sciences* in Italian, and Newton's *Optics* in English. Still, Latin was not yet dead as the learned language. Newton's greatest work, the *Mathematical Principles*, was written in Latin, as was also Huygens' chief work, the *Horologium*.

Aside from Newton, Huygens was probably the outstanding scientist of his day. Newton himself, in connection with problems of impact and elasticity, on which Huygens had worked, acknowledged that "Sir Christopher Wren, Dr. Wallis, and Mr. Huygens [are] the greatest geometers of our times . . ." (See p. 20a.) We have already remarked that Huygens' wave theory of light scored a decisive victory over Newton's corpuscular theory, until recent researches necessitated an uneasy compromise between the undular and the corpuscular theories. Huygens' genius achieved recognition in the many honors bestowed on him during his lifetime, in England, France, and Holland.

II

How does Huygens explain light in terms of wave motion? He begins by noting (p. 553b) that "light consists in the motion of some sort of matter." He adds almost at once (p. 554a) that the propagation of light cannot be "by any transport of matter coming to us from this [a luminous] object." Right here is the rejection of a corpuscular theory of light, since such a theory does hold that a luminous body sends out little particles which cause it to be luminous and to be seen.

Huygens' argument against the corpuscular theory contains two major points. First, the speed of light is so tremendous that Huygens does not believe solid corpuscles can travel that fast. This objection gains added force from the fact that a luminous body does not just send out one stream of corpuscles; on the contrary, corpuscles must shoot out from the light source in all directions. The second objection deals with the problem of two light rays crossing one another. If two rays, each consisting of a stream of corpuscles, were to cross one another, it would seem that the corpuscles of one must collide with the corpuscles of the other. This collision should result in some visible effect, such as the bending of one or both light rays. In fact, however, light rays invariably cross without causing the least interference with one another. "It is then in some other way that light spreads," Huygens concludes; "and that which can lead us to comprehend it is the knowledge which we have of the spreading of sound in the air." (See p. 554a.)

Sound is propagated as a wave in air. This leads Huygens to suppose that light, too, is propagated as a wave. But the medium in which the wave moves is not air. Sound cannot be heard without air. If, for instance, we put an alarm clock inside a bell jar and exhaust the air from the jar, then the sound of the clock cannot be heard. In fact, as the air is more and more nearly exhausted, the sound of the alarm becomes more and more faint. Light, on the other hand, does not depend on air for its propagation; it travels through a vacuum. If, in the alarm-clock experiment, the jar is made of glass, then as a vacuum is gradually produced, we still continue to see the clock as clearly as before. Furthermore, light rays from the stars reach us without difficulty, even though they travel through millions of miles of empty space.

But a wave motion necessarily requires that there be some medium in which the wave can exist. To speak of a wave in a vacuum is absurd. What is it that moves and how does this movement take place? Huygens answers this question as follows.

... I do not believe that this movement can be better explained than by supposing that all those of the luminous bodies which are liquid, such as flames, and apparently the sun and the stars, are composed of particles which float in a much more subtle medium which agitates them with great rapidity, and makes them strike against the particles of the ether which surrounds them, and which are much smaller than they. But I hold also that in luminous solids such as charcoal or metal made red-hot in the fire, this same movement is caused by the violent agitation of the particles of the metal or of the wood; those of them which are on the surface striking similarly against the ethereal matter. (p. 557b)

This "ether" is strictly invented for the sake of explaining the propagation of light. It has no other physical properties. It itself is invisible; it cannot be felt, smelled, or heard. It does not interfere in any way with the motions of bodies; it offers no resistance to bodies. In order that ether may serve as the medium for light waves, it needs, according to Huygens, only one property, namely, extreme elasticity. The more elastic a body is, the more nearly does it return to its original shape when a blow strikes it and indents it. A perfectly elastic body, if there were such, would return perfectly to its former shape. (See p. 559a.) The motion of light in Huygens' theory is caused by this kind of indentation and springing-back of the particles of the ether.

Now in applying this kind of movement to that which produces light there is nothing to hinder us from estimating the particles of the ether to be of a substance as nearly approaching to perfect hardness and possessing a springiness as prompt as we choose. (p. 559a)

The elasticity of the particles of the ether explains why light always travels with the same speed (p. 559b), why it is propagated in all directions from a light source (p. 560a), and why light rays can cross without interfering with one another (p. 561a). All this is accounted for by the fact that in wave motion from A to B, there is no one particle which travels from A to B. (See Fig. 1.) Instead, particle A acquires some motion, which it communicates to the adjacent particle A_1; A_1, in turn, because of its elasticity, communicates its motion to A_2, and so on. Finally, the next to last particle communicates its little bit of motion, its indentation and springing back, to the particle B. No particle, therefore, travels from A to B. What does travel from A to B is the elastic displacement; first A has it, then A_1, then A_2, and so on, until it reaches B. But this elastic displacement is not a particle, nor is it a thing of any kind. It is a condition of a particle; namely, the condition of being first indented and then springing back. Thus what travels from A to B is an event or occurrence.

FIG. 1

We can liken the particles A, A_1, A_2, ... B to a row of men. Suppose that the last man, B, is ordered to raise his right hand when someone next to him raises his right hand. Now let the first man, A, raise his right hand. If this makes A_1 raise his hand, which in turn makes A_2 raise his hand, and so on, the signal will eventually get to B, and he will raise his right hand. Without the intervening men A_1, A_2, ... the only way in which the signal could be communicated from A to B would be for A to run over and stand next to B. This involves someone changing position. The first way does not require any person to change position. What travels down the line of men is an event, namely, the raising of right hands.

This is how Huygens conceives the propagation of light. "The propagation," Huygens writes, "consists nowise in the transport of those particles but merely in a small agitation which they cannot help communicating to those surrounding ..." (p. 560b)

III

We have mentioned that the *Treatise on Light* was published before Newton's *Optics*. The book was known to Newton, as is indicated by the fact that on page 522b he refers to it by name. Nevertheless, Newton rejected the theory that light is propagated in waves. He tells us some of his reasons for this rejection in Book III, Query 28:

If light consisted only in pression propagated without actual motion, it would not be able to agitate and heat the bodies which refract and reflect it. If it consisted in motion propagated to all distances in an instant, it would require an infinite force every moment, in every shining particle, to generate that motion. (pp. 525b-526a)

These two objections, it should be noted, do not actually apply to Huygens' theory. Huygens does not consider the motion of light to be caused by pressure, but by a slight motion of particles. (This eliminates the first objection.) And though Huygens thinks that it consists in "motion propagated to all distances," he does not think this takes place instantaneously. (This takes care of the second objection.) But Newton has a third objection, and it does apply to Huygens' theory:

And if it consisted in pression or motion, propagated either in an instant or in time, it would bend into the shadow. For pression or motion cannot be propagated in a fluid in right lines, beyond an obstacle which stops part of the motion, but will bend and spread every way into the quiescent medium which lies beyond the obstacle. (p. 526a)

What Newton questions here is the ability of the wave theory to explain the rectilinear propagation of light. Why does light travel in straight lines? Why, furthermore, does light not bend around an obstacle, as sound does? A very small object can prevent the rays of a star from reaching our eye; on the other hand, a very much larger object cannot prevent sound waves from reaching our ear, though it may lessen the intensity of the sound. Newton apparently thought his question was unanswerable; for, after posing it and a few related ones having to do with the ether, he begins his next query as follows: "Are not the rays of light very small bodies emitted from shining substances? For such bodies will pass through uniform mediums in right lines without bending into the shadow, which is the nature of the rays of light." (See p. 529b.)

Huygens, however, offers an explanation for the rectilinear propagation of light. The explanation employs what is now known as "Huygens' principle." The principle states that the wave spreading from the original light source is not the only wave. Each particle of the ether, as it becomes agitated by the wave passing through it, in turn starts to produce another little wave or wavelet. What finally reaches an object to illuminate it is not a simple wave, but rather a "wave front," made up of many waves.

... each particle of matter, in which a wave spreads, ought not to communicate its motion only to the next particle which is in the straight line drawn from the luminous point, but . . . it also imparts some of it necessarily to all the others which touch it and which oppose themselves to its movement. So it arises that around each particle there is made a wave of which that particle is the centre. (pp. 561b-562a)

In the diagram on page 562, Huygens illustrates this principle. Let A be a light source. (See Fig. 2.) After a certain time t_1, the wave emanating from A will reach point B. But the wave will not, of course, stop at B but will go on, so that after more

time has elapsed, say at time t_2, the wave that started from A
will have got to point C. Meanwhile, however, the particle of
the ether located at point B will
start its own wave through the
ether. The wave originating
from point A is represented by
the arc of the circle DCEF; this
is its position at time t_2. The
wave that started at B at time t_1
will also have got to point C by
the time t_2, since both waves
travel equally rapidly. How-

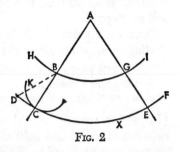

FIG. 2

ever, the two waves will not coincide; the circle KCL represents
the wavelet originating at point B, at time t_2. At time t_2, therefore, the original wave and the secondary wavelet reinforce
each other at the point C. At other points, the two waves do
not reinforce each other; for instance, at time t_2, there is no
reinforcement of the two waves in the direction BD. For the
original wave at t_2 in this direction has reached D, while the
secondary wavelet has reached only K.

It can easily be seen that the original wave at the point C
will be reinforced by all the wavelets started by ether particles
along the line AC. All such wavelets will reach C at the same
time. The wavelets starting from AC will not reach any other
point together. It can also be seen that any other point on the
original wave, such as X, will be reinforced by all the wavelets starting up from the points in the line AX. These wavelets
will not reinforce each other at any other point, and X also
receives no reinforcement from the other luminous points. An
original wave reinforced by secondary waves, represented
here by the line DCEF, is called a wave front.

Now let BG be an opening in an otherwise non-transparent
screen HBGI. The preceding discussion explains why the light
emanating from A will at time t_2 be found at CE, while the
area to the left of CB and to the right of GE will be in shadow.
Only along CE do all the waves reinforce each other. (Actually
it can be shown that in the areas to the left of CB and to the
right of GE the waves not only do not reinforce each other
but tend to cancel each other. Huygens, however, does not

show this.) Since there is no reinforcement of waves to the left of AC or to the right of AE, light does not "bend into the shadow." If an obstacle is placed at CE, all the light from A will be stopped.

Since each point like X is reinforced by all the wavelets starting from points along the line AX, and by no others,

. . . each little portion of the wave necessarily advances following the straight line which comes from the luminous point. Thus, then, we may take the rays of light as if they were straight lines. (p. 563a)

(In passing, we may remark that the reason for the different behavior of sound and light in the matter of bending into the shadow is to be found in the difference of wave lengths.)

Even if the wave theory can explain the rectilinear propagation of light, Newton still has a fourth objection to it. This objection is directed against the existence of the ether which is necessary for the propagation of the waves. The ether, being material, should offer some resistance to the motion of bodies. But the planets and other heavenly bodies seem to experience no retardation whatever in the course of thousands of years. Hence, Newton thinks, the ether, which he calls a fluid, should be rejected.

A dense fluid can be of no use for explaining the phenomena of Nature, the motions of the planets and comets being better explained without it. It serves only to disturb and retard the motions of those great bodies, and make the frame of Nature languish; and in the pores of bodies it serves only to stop the vibrating motions of their parts, wherein their heat and activity consists. And as it is of no use, and hinders the operations of Nature, and makes her languish, so there is no evidence for its existence; and, therefore, it ought to be rejected. And if it be rejected, the hypotheses that light consists in pression or motion, propagated through such a medium, are rejected with it. (p. 528b)

Huygens seems to ignore this difficulty.

IV

Now let us see how the wave theory explains the phenomenon of refraction. Huygens devotes Chapter III to this. He makes the initial assumption that light travels more slowly in a medium than in a vacuum, either because the light wave which is transmitted through the ether has to detour around the particles of matter composing the medium (p. 568b) or because the particles of matter are less elastic than the particles of ether (p. 569a). "In which different velocity of light," Huygens writes, "I shall show the cause of refraction to consist." (p. 568b)

In the diagram on page 570, AC is a "wave front" falling on the medium. (See Fig. 3.) AC is so far from its light source that it may be considered as a straight line, instead of a circle, as the wave front DCEF was in the diagram on page 562. AC may be as small as we please; let it be considered as the width of a ray of light.

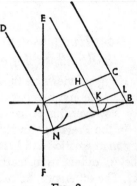

FIG. 3

Huygens now assumes that light in the refracting medium (below AB) travels two-thirds as fast as in air (above AB). Hence, while the portion C of the wave front travels from C to B, in air, the portion A will travel in the medium a distance equal to two-thirds of CB. Or, more correctly, a wave will start out from A which in the time taken by C to reach B will advance a distance equal to two-thirds of CB.

Around A, therefore, describe a circle with a radius equal to two-thirds CB. Next consider a portion H of the original wave front. It reaches the medium at point K. Draw KL parallel to AC. Then while part C of the original wave front travels from L to B, a wave will start from K and reach a distance equal to two-thirds of LB. Around K, therefore, describe a circle with a radius equal to two-thirds LB. Do this for several other points between A and C. The wave front will then be found along the line which is tangent to all the circles drawn around A and such points as K.

It can easily be shown that the sine of the angle of incidence will be to the sine of the angle of refraction in the ratio of 3:2—thereby verifying Snell's Law. For angle CAB is equal to angle DAE, the angle of incidence. And its sine is $\dfrac{CB}{AB}$. And the angle ABN is equal to angle FAN, the angle of refraction. And its sine is $\dfrac{AN}{AB}$. Thus the two sines are to each other as $\dfrac{CB}{AN}$ or as 3:2.

V

Does Huygens express any views about the method and philosophy of science?

Huygens' views on these matters are confined to the Preface and to the first two pages of Chapter I. In spite of their brevity, however, his remarks are of the first importance.

In the Preface, Huygens indicates how physics, though using mathematics and being in many ways similar to it, nevertheless differs from mathematics (or "geometry," as he calls it). The difference, he tells us, arises from the character of the principles. The principles of mathematics are absolutely fixed and incontestable. Thus, in Euclid's *Elements,* there is no proof or argument for the definitions, axioms, and postulates. Everything follows from these principles. But here, in optics or in mathematical physics generally, it is just the other way around.

... The principles are verified by the conclusions to be drawn from them; the nature of these things not allowing of this being done otherwise. It is always possible to attain thereby to a degree of probability which very often is scarcely less than complete proof. (p. 551b)

In other words, in natural science hypotheses are made, and then these hypotheses are tested by investigating whether what a hypothesis predicts is actually found to be the case in phenomena.

... If all these proofs of probability are met with in that which I propose to discuss, as it seems to me they are, this ought to be a very strong confirmation of the success of my inquiry; and it must be ill if the facts are not pretty much as I represent them. (pp. 551b-552a)

An even more interesting statement occurs near the beginning of Chapter I. Huygens asserts that "light consists in the motion of some sort of matter" (p. 553b). He then reviews the evidence for this assertion and concludes:

This is assuredly the mark of motion, at least in the true philosophy, in which one conceives the causes of all natural effects in terms of mechanical motions. This, in my opinion, we must necessarily do, or else renounce all hopes of ever comprehending anything in physics. (p. 554a)

This is a remarkable statement. We see that Huygens thinks of himself as pursuing a "true philosophy" or true science of physics. This science is both *experimental* and *mathematical* in character. Huygens adds a third characteristic of the true science of physics: it must also be *mechanical*. No natural effect is satisfactorily explained in this science unless it has been shown to be due to the motions of material particles in accord with Newton's laws of motion.

This kind of mechanistic physics enjoyed a spectacular success during the eighteenth and nineteenth centuries, when it seemed as though no physical phenomena could resist mechanical explanation. Phenomena of light, sound, and heat were explained mechanically. So were the phenomena of fluids at rest or in motion. Even large-scale astronomical phenomena seemed to be explainable by the same principles as the microscopic phenomena inside atoms. In the twentieth century, however, mechanistic physics lost its pre-eminence, largely because it failed to explain certain sub-atomic phenomena. Relativity theory and quantum mechanics replaced it as the dominant part of physics.

How is the speed of light determined?

Huygens tells us that he had supposed that light is not transmitted instantaneously, although he had no actual proof of this. "But," he writes, "that which I employed only as a hypothesis, has recently received great seemingness as an established truth by the ingenious proof of Mr. Römer . . ." (p. 556a).

The speed of light is so great that it is hardly surprising that for a long time it was thought that its speed is infinite; that is, that light takes no time whatsoever to travel from one point to the other. In Galileo's *Two New Sciences* (First Day), Simplicio states this view:

> Everyday experience shows that the propagation of light is instantaneous; for when we see a piece of artillery fired, at great distance, the flash reaches our eyes without lapse of time; but the sound reaches the ear only after a noticeable interval. (Vol. 28, p. 148d)

Galileo correctly points out that this proves nothing except that light travels very rapidly. He suggests an experiment for determining the speed of light. Galileo proposes that two men with lanterns stand opposite each other, and that the second one turn his light on when he sees the light of the first one. "Let the two experimenters," he writes,

> ... take up positions separated by a distance of two or three miles and let them perform the same experiment at night, noting carefully whether the exposures and occultations occur in the same manner as at short distances; if they do, we may safely conclude that the propagation of light is instantaneous; but if time is required at a distance of three miles which, considering the going of one light and the coming of the other, really amounts to six, then the delay ought to be easily observable. (Vol. 28, p. 149b)

We know, of course, that the speed of light is very great, so that the time it takes to traverse a mere six miles could not possibly be measured by Galileo's method. Römer's method, which Huygens reproduces on pages 556-557, succeeded because Römer employed the diameter of the earth's orbit as the distance over which light travels.

Römer's method consisted in observing a celestial phenomenon (the eclipse of one of the satellites of Jupiter) from

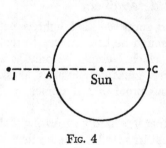

Fig. 4

opposite parts on the earth's orbit, such as A and C in Figure 4. We know how long it takes for the satellite to complete one revolution. Therefore we can predict when it should be eclipsed again. Thus, let us suppose that I is the satellite and that we observe the beginning of its eclipse from the earth at point A of its orbit. Let another eclipse of the satellite be due to begin when the earth is at C. It is found, however, that when the earth is at C, the eclipse has not yet begun. This is due to the fact that the light had to traverse the additional distance AC. Huygens gives Römer's figures, which indicated that light takes about 23 minutes to travel this distance. Actually, this is off by quite a bit. Light from the sun travels to the earth (that is, half the distance AC) in somewhat over 8 minutes. Römer's method was subject to inaccuracies because it depended on a precise knowledge of astronomical distances, which had not been perfectly measured in his day.

Modern methods for measuring the speed of light by non-astronomical means were developed by Fizeau (1849), Foucault (1862), and Michelson (1878), among others. All these methods are discussed very fully in the article VELOCITY OF LIGHT in *Encyclopaedia Britannica*. The actual speed of light has been found to be very nearly 300,000 km. per second ($3 \cdot 10^{10}$ cm./sec.), which is approximately 186,000 miles per second.

If a body can travel with only one speed in one medium, and a different speed in another medium, what is the fastest way for it to go from a point in the one medium to a given point in the other medium?

The fastest way to go is to follow Snell's Law. Huygens shows this on pages 573-575. That is, if a body has to go from a point A in air to a point C in water, and if its speed in air is to its speed in water as 3:2, then the fastest way of getting from A to C is to go in such a way that the sine of the angle of incidence is to the angle of refraction as 3:2. Huygens shows this by proving that any other path would take longer to traverse.

Let us make this "principle of

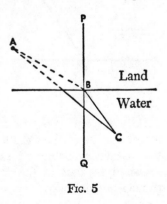

Fig. 5

least action" clear to ourselves by an example. Suppose a man is standing on a beach, at the point A, and wants to reach a point C in the water (say a tied-up boat) in the least time. (See Fig. 5.) He will not accomplish this by heading for C in a straight line. Since he can walk much more rapidly than he can swim, it is easy to see that it will be to his advantage to walk more than to swim. He should therefore head for the point B, which is such that the sine of the angle ABP is to the sine of the angle CBQ as his walking speed is to his swimming speed.

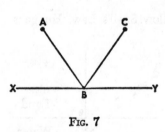

If this does not seem persuasive, imagine that both point A and point C are very near the shoreline and that AX = CY. (See Fig. 6.) Then, if the man headed straight for C, he would spend half his time walking and half swimming. Since he can walk so much faster than he can swim, it is obviously faster for

FIG. 6

him to head for some such point as B, which enables him to spend most of his time walking, leaving him to swim only the short distance BC.

Is the law of reflection also an instance of the principle of

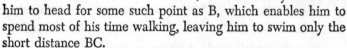

"least action"? Suppose someone is required to go from A in one medium to C in the same medium, but in such a way that the line XBY be touched. Is there a faster way of reaching C from A than by making the angle of incidence equal to the angle of reflection?

FIG. 7

Do you think Huygens would be willing to say that the reason for the truth of the laws of refraction and reflection is that nature avoids unnecessary effort?

Can it be part of the "true" mechanistic physics to use principles that endow nature with desires, efforts, or goals?

The following questions are designed to help you test the thoroughness of your reading. Each question is to be answered by giving a page or pages of the reading assignment. Answers will be found on page 224 of this Reading Plan.

1 Why are eclipses of the moon not suitable for measuring the speed of light?

2 Does Huygens' explanation of reflection require that the reflecting surface be perfectly smooth and even?

3 How does Huygens explain the transparency of certain bodies (that is, the fact that they permit light to pass through them)?

4 What are the phenomena of refraction by the atmospheric air which Huygens enumerates?

5 Suppose a light ray starts in water and travels toward the surface separating the water from air. Must such a ray always be refracted into the air?

6 When a wave of light reaches the eye, where do we judge that the object generating the wave is located?

LAVOISIER

Elements of Chemistry

Preface, Part I, Ch. I–VIII

Vol. 45, pp. 1–33

This reading reminds us once again that scientific inquiry is concerned with the ordinary things of the ordinary world. This is perhaps even clearer in chemistry than it is in physics. The chemist's business is to find out the elements that constitute the things around us. What is the constitution of wood, of sugar, of the rocks on the ground, even of air? Almost every high-school boy knows that the ordinary air which we breathe is composed largely of oxygen, but also contains nitrogen. What not every high-school boy knows is that this was discovered by Antoine Lavoisier.

Indeed, it was Lavoisier who invented the very names "oxygen" and "nitrogen." He considered the naming of things as important for the scientist as it was for Adam in the Garden of Eden. Names, for him, are intimately connected with the knowledge of things; hence the advance of science goes hand in hand with an advance in nomenclature. The now fashionable notion that a science is a language, involving a systematic, precise arrangement of terms, was proclaimed in the 18th century by the Abbé de Condillac and Lavoisier. A large part of the *Elements of Chemistry* is devoted to a systematic naming of the chemical elements.

Turn to the plates depicting the experimental apparatus of Lavoisier, at the end of the Third Part, and you will appreciate what a skilful and patient experimenter he was. Perhaps even more than Newton's *Optics*, this book is a record of experiments painstakingly performed. In his search for the constitution of air, Lavoisier did not hesitate to heat mercury for twelve successive days. He realized that without experiments the science of chemistry is nothing. "Such as wish to acquire accurate knowledge of the science of chemistry . . . should familiarise themselves to the employment of apparatus, and to the performance of experiments by actual experience." There is Lavoisier's advice and also warning to us. The student of chemistry cannot expect to learn it just from books; he must turn to the things themselves.

Fifteenth Reading

I

Our last reading in this Plan is also the first one to deal with chemistry. This is not just an accident. Chemistry in the modern sense of the word dates only from the time of Robert Boyle (1627-1691), Joseph Priestley (1733-1804), and Antoine Lavoisier himself (1743-1794). Before this, investigations into the constitution of matter and the changes of bodies were made for the sake of alchemy, from which scientific chemistry emerged. The alchemists in their endeavors to make gold from other substances paid little attention to theory. For the most part, they relied on Aristotle's doctrine that all terrestrial bodies are made up out of four elements (earth, air, fire, and water), or on Paracelsus' doctrine that there are just three principles, namely salt, sulfur, and mercury. Such doctrines, of course, give a certain plausibility to the view that a compound body can be changed into another compound body, since both are made up of the same elements or principles.

Robert Boyle's *Sceptical Chymist*, published in 1661, did much to show that neither the doctrine of the four elements nor that of the three principles could hold up in the light of experiments and observations. By Lavoisier's time, it was clear that the material constitution of things was much more complex, and needed to be investigated experimentally.

Lavoisier's work contributed greatly to the advance of chemistry. In the first part of the *Elements of Chemistry*, he develops the correct theory of combustion. In the second part, he exhibits his system of naming the compounds formed in chemical reactions of elements. His system was so reasonable that we still follow it today. In the third part, Lavoisier describes his experimental apparatus; this was of importance in his day when there was no tradition of scientific chemical experimentation.

To get an idea of the advance made by Lavoisier, compare his discovery and analysis of oxygen (in Chapter 3) with the following account (taken from *The Sceptical Chymist*), in which Boyle has a philosopher of Aristotle's school give alleged evidence for the existence of the four elements:

If you but consider a piece of green wood burning in a chimney, you will readily discern in the disbanded parts of it the four elements, of which we teach it and other mixt bodies to be composed. The fire discovers itself in the flame by its own light; the smoake by ascending to the top of the chimney, and there readily vanishing into air, like a river losing itself in the sea, sufficiently manifests to what element it belongs and gladly returnes. The water in its own form boiling and hissing at the ends of the burning wood betrays itself to more than one of our senses; and the ashes by their weight, their firiness, and their dryness, put it past doubt that they belong to the element of earth.[1]

II

Let us consider the title of the book. As Euclid entitled his work the *Elements of Geometry*, so Lavoisier entitles his the *Elements of Chemistry*. Other scientists, we have seen in the course of this Reading Plan, have shown their indebtedness to Euclid by imitating his method and dividing their works into Definitions, Axioms, and Propositions. But Lavoisier, in spite of the similarity of titles, does not cast his treatise in Euclidean form.

The Preface gives us a hint of the reason why Lavoisier is so little concerned with mathematics. Whereas such men as Descartes, Newton, and Huygens had looked to mathematical reasoning for the advancement of knowledge, Lavoisier looks to the improvement of language as most important. He thinks that by improving the language men use, he will thereby improve their thought. The quotation at the end of the Preface shows the importance that Lavoisier attaches not only to proper experimentation and observation, but also to proper language. The words are those of the philosopher Condillac.

---

[1] Everyman's Library, New York: E. P. Dutton & Co., 1937, p. 21.

. . . the sciences have made progress, because philosophers have applied themselves with more attention to observe and have communicated to their language that precision and accuracy which they have employed in their observations. In correcting their language they reason better. (p. 7c)

III

In the first chapter, Lavoisier discusses the effects and causes of heat. At once we see his method at work and can detect his intellectual and scientific attitude. It is clear that he is influenced—as any scientist of the 18th century would have to be—by Newton's work. This is evidenced by the attention he pays to attraction and repulsion.

But what is more interesting is that he conceives the cause of heat to be a substance—an elastic fluid which he names *caloric*. Unless heat is caused by a "real and material substance," Lavoisier finds it difficult to explain the phenomena associated with heat, especially the expansion of bodies that are heated.

"This substance," he writes,

whatever it is, being the cause of heat, or, in other words, the sensation which we call *warmth* being caused by the accumulation of this substance, we cannot, in strict language, distinguish it by the term *heat;* because the same name would then very improperly express both cause and effect. . . . Wherefore, we have distinguished the cause of heat, or that exquisitely elastic fluid which produces it, by the term of *caloric.* Besides that this expression fulfils our object in the system which we have adopted, it possesses this further advantage, that it accords with every species of opinion, since, strictly speaking, we are not obliged to suppose this to be a real substance; it being sufficient, as will more clearly appear in the sequel of this work, that it be considered as the repulsive cause, whatever that may be, which separates the particles of matter from each other, so that we are still at liberty to investigate its effects in an abstract and mathematical manner. (p. 10a-b)

Caloric must be invisible (in fact, not detectable by any of the five senses) and imponderable (weightless). The most careful experiments do not show that a hot body is heavier than a cold one, as it would have to be if caloric had weight. The theory of caloric, though it may seem childish to us now, succeeds in explaining many of the phenomena of heat, such as the transfer of heat from a hotter to a cooler body. The theory had considerable difficulty in explaining certain other phenomena, such as the generation of heat by friction. It is now replaced by the molecular theory, which ascribes heat to the motion of molecules.

IV

It is difficult to appreciate Lavoisier's accomplishments, since much of what he discovered has become so familiar to us that we take it for granted and can hardly imagine that everyone did not always know these elementary things. The constitution of air is familiar to all of us. "Everyone" knows that it contains both oxygen and nitrogen, as well as small amounts of other gases. It was Lavoisier who discovered this, as he tells us in Chapter 3.

Lavoisier's first achievement is one that we are only too likely to forget: the realization that air is not necessarily an elementary body, but a mixture of several gases. Aristotle, and scholastic philosophy following Aristotle, had always considered air to be one of the four elements of things; that is, air was thought to be not further divisible into anything except smaller quantities of air.

A second step forward is the recognition that one and the same body may exist in several states; namely, that it may be solid, liquid, or gaseous. Whether a body is solid, liquid, or gaseous depends on the conditions of pressure and heat under which it exists. When a body has so much caloric fluid between its particles that the repulsive force of the caloric makes the body's particles fly apart, then the body is in its gaseous state. "Gas, therefore, in our nomenclature becomes a generic term, expressing the fullest degree of saturation in any body with caloric; being, in fact, a term expressive of a mode of existence" (p. 21d). If the earth were hotter than it is, therefore, more bodies would be in a gaseous state and the "air" surrounding the earth would contain other elements than it does now. A very slight rise in temperature, for instance, would suffice to make vapors out of liquids like alcohol. An intensely hot body, such as the sun, contains no solid core; all of its elements are in a gaseous state.

The third way in which Lavoisier's genius makes itself manifest is shown in the experiments whereby he determines what gases are in common air. Several experimental steps are involved. First, he heats mercury in a limited amount of air. The mercury turns into red particles of what we now call mercuric oxide. The air, he tells us, loses about one-sixth of its volume in this process. This loss is caused by the fact that the mercury has combined with the oxygen in the air to form the mercuric oxide. (See p. 17b-c.) Lavoisier describes the part of the air that does not enter into the combustion as follows:

The air which remained after the calcination of the mercury in this experiment, and which was reduced to $\frac{5}{6}$ of its former bulk, was no longer fit either for respiration or for combustion; animals being introduced into it were suffocated in a few seconds, and when a taper was plunged into it, it was extinguished as if it had been immersed into water. (p. 17d)

This experiment, therefore, isolates one of the component parts of air, namely that part which does not support combustion. We now call it nitrogen.

The second step consists in isolating the other part of air. In the first experiment, this part combined with mercury, forming a reddish compound. In the second experiment, Lavoisier applies heat to this reddish compound. His apparatus is designed to collect any gas that may be given off as the result of the heating. Under the influence of the heat, the reddish compound does, indeed, change; it reverts to the state of metallic mercury. In the course of this, "7 or 8 cubic inches of elastic fluid, greatly more capable of supporting both respiration and combustion than atmospherical air, were collected in the bell-glass" (pp. 17d-18a).

Lavoisier tells us what conclusions he draws from these two experiments:

In reflecting upon the circumstances of this experiment, we readily perceive that the mercury, during its calcination, absorbs the salubrious and respirable part of the air, or, to speak more strictly, the base of this respirable part; that the remaining air is a species of mephitis, incapable of supporting combustion or respiration; and consequently that atmospheric air is composed of two elastic fluids of different and opposite qualities. (p. 18a-b)

If we restate the above in more common and familiar language, it says the following: mercury, when heated in air, combines with the oxygen of the air, so that the result is mercuric oxide and nitrogen. Then, when the mercuric oxide is heated by itself, the oxygen is given off, so that the result is mercury and oxygen. The two experiments, therefore, leave us with three substances—mercury, nitrogen, and oxygen.

The third, and possibly most persuasive, step in this series of experiments consists in recombining the oxygen and nitrogen in proper proportions in order to obtain, again, the mixture of common atmospheric air. (See p. 18b.)

Lavoisier does not give names to these two gases in Chapter 3. He employs circumlocutions, such as "highly respirable air" for oxygen. Chapter 4 is given over to the subject of nomenclature. There he decides on the name "oxygen" because this substance is, in his opinion, what gives acids their properties. (Oxygen means "acid-producer.") In this opinion, Lavoisier is mistaken; not all acids contain oxygen. One of the most common acids which does not is hydrochloric or muriatic acid, made up of hydrogen and chlorine only. (See p. 27a-b.) Nevertheless, the name "oxygen" has stuck.

The other gas which makes up atmospheric air Lavoisier calls "azote." This name, too, is derived from the Greek; it is used to signify that this gas cannot support life and is, in fact, lethal. This name, though quite appropriate, has not been retained. Lavoisier himself notes (p. 22b) that this gas was shown "to compose a part of the nitric acid, which gives as good reason to have called it *nitrogen.*" "Nitrogen" is, of course, the name used nowadays.

V

What is the utility of introducing imaginary substances like Lavoisier's caloric and Huygens' ether into science?

Is it helpful or harmful to the progress of science to explain phenomena by something for which there is no experimental evidence? The only reason for saying that there is an ether or that there is a caloric fluid is that they are needed to explain the phenomena of light and heat. But are not such explanations contrary to Newton's advice not to frame unnecessary hypotheses? Lavoisier, when confronted with the need to account for the cause of heat, ascribed it to a caloric fluid. Newton, when confronted with the question of what caused the gravitational phenomena, wrote:

But hitherto I have not been able to discover the cause of those properties of gravity from phenomena, and I frame no hypotheses; for whatever is not deduced from the phenomena is to be called an hypothesis; and hypotheses, whether metaphysical or physical, whether of occult qualities or mechanical, have no place in experimental philosophy. In this philosophy particular propositions are inferred from the phenomena, and afterwards rendered general by induction. (Vol. 34, p. 371b)

It certainly seems as if both Huygens and Lavoisier ignore Newton's words. They have, however, good reasons for this. In Huygens' case, we must remember that the ether is not introduced capriciously. Ether makes it possible to account for the propagation of light by waves, and this in turn makes it possible to explain the experimentally confirmed fact that light travels more slowly in a denser medium than it does in a rarer.

Lavoisier is very cautious and tentative about the real existence of caloric. Indeed, he says, in a passage which we have already quoted, that "we are not obliged to suppose this to be a real substance." It suffices for his purpose that "caloric" denotes "the repulsive cause, whatever that may be, which separates the particles of matter from each other ..."

Why, then, does Lavoisier introduce the notion of a caloric fluid at all? It is for the sake of making it easier to understand the phenomena of heat. He writes: "It is difficult to comprehend these phenomena, without admitting them as the effects of a real and material substance ..." How valid is this argument? Are physical phenomena really more easily understood by means of substances as causes? Is this a more comprehensible mode of explanation than one which employs "forces" or "centers of force?" Is a substance like caloric any more or less hypothetical than, say, the force of gravity?

What is the role of analysis and synthesis in chemistry?

Lavoisier writes:

Chemistry affords two general methods of determining the constituent principles of bodies, the method of analysis, and that of synthesis. When, for instance, by combining water with alcohol we form the species of liquor called, in commercial language, brandy or spirit of wine, we certainly have a right to conclude that brandy, or spirit of wine, is composed of alcohol combined with water. We can produce the same result by the analytical method; and in general it ought to be considered as a principle in chemical science never to rest satisfied without both these species of proofs. (p. 17a)

Lavoisier gives us an instance of both the analytical and synthetic method when he deals with the question of the constitution of the air. He analyzes it as being composed of oxygen and nitrogen; then he recombines these two gases in the proper proportions and so re-obtains air.

Lavoisier may be right in saying that it is always desirable to employ both analysis and synthesis. Suppose, however, that only one of these two processes can be carried out and not the other. Does this throw any doubt on the previous results? For example, let analysis have shown that water is composed of two parts of hydrogen and one part of oxygen. Now put hydrogen and oxygen, in those proportions, in a container. Do these two gases combine to form water? No, they do not. As a matter of act, nothing at all happens. Does this, then, show that the analysis was incorrect? Again, the answer is no.

By the introduction of an electric spark, the hydrogen can be made to burn and then water is formed from the two gases. Does this then show that the analysis was correct, because it is confirmed by synthesis? Perhaps so, but does not this also raise other problems? For instance, what are we to say about the introduction of the electric spark? Does this in any way alter the experimental situation? Is the synthesis, in other words, a pure synthesis when it needs some additional agent to trigger it?

LAVOISIER: *Elements of Chemistry* 221

What does Lavoisier substitute for the four elementary bodies, air, water, earth, fire?

He shows us that these four elements are by no means simple, and that they are not the ultimate building blocks of matter. Let us look at the four elements one by one.

Air: We have already remarked that Lavoisier shows that the common atmospheric air is composed of at least two gases, oxygen and nitrogen.

Water: In Chapter VIII, Lavoisier describes how he decomposed water. It, too, is therefore not an element. It is composed of oxygen and hydrogen.

Earth: The name "earth" entered into the appellation of many substances found naturally, such as salts and metallic ores. This was in accord with the Aristotelian theory that everything heavy was predominantly earth. For instance, lime was called "aerated calcareous earth." For the confusion of names employing the word "earth," Lavoisier substitutes names indicative of the chemical constitution of the substances they name. Thus lime, in the system derived from Lavoisier, is called calcium oxide.

Earth, instead of being an elementary body, therefore is seen to be, in Lavoisier's system, a name that covers metals, non-metals, and salts—in fact, almost everything except gases.

Fire: If by this is meant the cause of heat, then Lavoisier substitutes the substance caloric for it. The process of combustion in the new system is seen to be an instance of oxidation.

What is an element in Lavoisier's system? How can one be sure that what is thought to be an element really is one? Can there be a least part of matter?

Is caloric an element? Since chemists no longer believe in the existence of caloric, do you think it is possible that some of the other elements also are not real?

The following questions are designed to help you test the thoroughness of your reading. Each question is to be answered by giving a page or pages of the reading assignment. Answers will be found on page 224 of this Reading Plan.

1 According to Lavoisier what is the general condition for sensation?

2 What are the chemical properties of oxygen?

3 How does Lavoisier's nomenclature distinguish between the two different acids formed by the lesser and greater oxidation of some elements such as phosphorus and sulfur?

4 What substances does Lavoisier use in order to separate water into oxygen and hydrogen?

5 What does Lavoisier propose to use as the measure of caloric freed in a chemical reaction?

6 What happens when a volatile liquid is placed in conditions of greatly lessened air pressure?

7 What is Lavoisier's opinion concerning the number of elements?

8 Does Lavoisier succeed in combining oxygen and hydrogen to form water?

ANSWERS
to self-testing questions

First Reading

1. Prop. 4, p. 4a–b
   Prop. 8, pp. 6b–7a
   Prop. 26, pp. 16a–17b
2. Prop. 16, pp. 10b–11a
3. Def. 15, p. 1b
4. Prop. 20, p. 12a–b
5. Prop. 3
   Prop. 1
   Post. 1
   Prop. 8
6. Prop. 22, pp. 13b–14a

Second Reading

1. Props. 32, 37, 38, 39, 40, 42, 44, 46, 47
2. Prop. 33, p. 20b
3. Prop. 43, p. 25a–b
4. Prop. 30, p. 19a
5. Prop. 32, pp. 19b–20a
6. Props. 27 & 28, pp. 17b–18b

Third Reading

1. Yes. Prop. 5, Cor. 2, p. 503a–b
2. Yes. Prop. 6, pp. 503b–504a
3. Yes. Post. 5, p. 502a
4. Within the hemisphere. Post. 7, p. 502b
5. Keep the distances from the fulcrum the same, but increase the weight 12 to 15. *Or,* keep the weights the same, but change the distance 10 to 8. Prop. 6, pp. 503b–504a
6. Yes. Post. 4, p. 502a

Fourth Reading

1. 813a–c

2. odd-times even, pp. 816b–817d
3. odd, p. 816a
4. 814b
5. 818b–c
6. 814b

Fifth Reading

1. One-third. Prop. 5, p. 540a–b
2. Post. 1, p. 538a
3. It is spherical. Prop. 1, p. 538a
4. Yes. Post. 1, p. 538a
5. True, Props. 3, 6, 7, pp. 539a–b, 540b–541a
6. Yes. Post. 1, p. 538a; Prop. 7, p. 541a

Sixth Reading

1. 12b–13b
2. 7b–8a
3. 5a–b
4. Slower. p. 87b
5. At 90° from apsides, p. 88a–b
6. No. Distance between sun and earth has nothing to do with the seasons. Ptolemy shows that the sun is at the apogee (according to his observation) approximately 25 days before the summer tropic, that is, about May 26.
7. No. He puts astronomy first. pp. 5b–6a

Seventh Reading

1. Yes. p. 510b
2. 530a–b

223

3. 512a–b
4. 519a
5. 511b
6. 505a–b, 521b–525a

Eighth Reading

1. 852a–b
2. The sun must be in the center of the world because of (1) its dignity and (2) its function in the universe. p. 857b
3. 887a
4. The elliptical figure of the planets' orbits. pp. 852b–853a, 966b–967b
5. 908a–b
6. 887b–888a
7. Copernicus, Tycho Brahe, William Gilbert. p. 850a

Ninth Reading

1. 203d–205a
2. They are as the odd numbers (1, 3, 5, 7). p. 206d
3. 204b–d
4. 201a–202a
5. 197c–d
6. 208a–b

Tenth Reading

1. 108d
2. 111b
3. 114a–b
4. 140b
5. 112c–d
6. 140b–c
7. 151a–b

Eleventh Reading

1. 385b
2. 386b–387a

3. 388a
4. 383a–b, 389a
5. 388a
6. 386a
7. 389a

Twelfth Reading

1. 9b
2. 15a
3. 6b
4. 15a–16b
5. 18a–19a
6. 371a–b
7. 270a–b
8. 23b–24a

Thirteenth Reading

1. 379a
2. 384b–385b
3. 541b
4. 542a–543a
5. 379b
6. 403b–404a
7. 388b

Fourteenth Reading

1. 544b–556a
2. 566a–b
3. 566b–569b
4. 575a–b
5. 572a–573b
6. 576b

Fifteenth Reading

1. 14a–b
2. 18a
3. 25c–26b
4. 30c–31b
5. 14b–c
6. 11a–c
7. 3b–4a
8. 32a–33a

ADDITIONAL READINGS

I. Works included in *Great Books of the Western World*

Vol. 7: PLATO, *Timaeus*

    8: ARISTOTLE, *Posterior Analytics; Physics; On the Heavens; On Generation and Corruption*

  11: EUCLID, *Elements,* Books II-XIII

  11: APOLLONIUS, *On Conic Sections,* Books I-III

  11: ARCHIMEDES, *Measurement of a Circle; The Sand-Reckoner*

  12: LUCRETIUS, *On the Nature of Things*

  16: KEPLER, *Harmonies of the World,* Book V

  28: GILBERT, *On the Loadstone*

  31: DESCARTES, *Geometry*

  33: PASCAL, *Preface to the Treatise on the Vacuum; New Experiments Concerning the Vacuum; Treatise on the Equilibrium of Liquids and on the Weight of the Mass of the Air; On Geometrical Demonstration; Treatise on the Arithmetical Triangle; Correspondence With Fermat on the Theory of Probabilities*

45: FOURIER, *Analytical Theory of Heat,* Chapters I-II

45: FARADAY, *Experimental Researches in Electricity*

II. Other Works

A. Some of the Basic Documents in Mathematics

(Because many of the great mathematical works are short monographs, often in foreign languages and untranslated, they are most easily approached through collections such as the following two)

NEWMAN, J. R. (ed.), *The World of Mathematics,* 4 vols. New York: Simon and Schuster, 1956

SMITH, DAVID E. (ed.), *Source Book in Mathematics.* Cambridge: Harvard University Press, 1956

(Since we have mentioned non-Euclidean geometries at some length in the first guide, the following two books may be of special interest)

LOBACHEVSKI, NICHOLAS, *Geometrical Researches on the Theory of Parallels.* Trans. by George B. Halsted. New York: Dover Publications, 1954

SACCHERI, GIROLAMO, *Euclides Vindicatus.* Ed. and trans. by George B. Halsted. Chicago: Open Court Publishing Co., 1920

B. Histories of Mathematics

BALL, W. W. ROUSE, *A Short Account of the History of Mathematics.* London: Macmillan and Co., 1927

BELL, ERIC T., *The Development of Mathematics.* New York: McGraw-Hill, 1945; *Men of Mathematics.* New York: Simon and Schuster, 1937

CAJORI, FLORIAN, *History of Mathematics*. New York: Macmillan Co., 1924

HEATH, SIR THOMAS L., *A History of Greek Mathematics*. London: Oxford University Press, 1921

HOFMAN, JOSEPH E., *The History of Mathematics*. Trans. by F. Gaynor and H. O. Midonick. New York: Philosophical Library, 1957

SMITH, DAVID E., *History of Mathematics*, 2 vols. New York: Dover Publications, 1958

STRUIK, DIRK J., *A Concise History of Mathematics*. New York: Dover Publications, 1948

C. Mathematical Method and Philosophy of Mathematics

CARNAP, RUDOLF, *Foundations of Logic and Mathematics*. International Encyclopedia of Unified Science, Vol. I, No. 3. Chicago: University of Chicago Press, 1953

COURANT, RICHARD and ROBBINS, HERBERT, *What is Mathematics?* New York: Oxford University Press, 1951

FREGE, GOTTLOB, *The Foundations of Arithmetic*. Trans. by J. L. Austin. New York: Philosophical Library, 1950

HILBERT, DAVID, *The Foundations of Geometry*. Trans. by E. J. Townsend. LaSalle, Illinois: Open Court Publishing Co., 1938

JOURDAIN, P. E. B., *The Nature of Mathematics*. London: Thomas Nelson & Sons, 1919

KASNER, EDWARD and NEWMAN, JAMES, *Mathematics and the Imagination*. New York: Simon and Schuster, 1940

RUSSELL, BERTRAND, *Introduction to Mathematical Philosophy.* New York: Macmillan Co., 1924; *The Principles of Mathematics.* New York: W. W. Norton & Co.

WEYL, HERMANN, *Philosophy of Mathematics and Natural Science.* Princeton: Princeton University Press, 1949

WHITEHEAD, ALFRED NORTH, *An Introduction to Mathematics.* New York: Henry Holt and Company, 1911

WIENER, PHILIP P. (ed.), *Readings in Philosophy of Science.* New York: Charles Scribner's Sons, 1953

D. Some of the Basic Documents in Natural Science

BOYLE, ROBERT, *The Sceptical Chymist.* New York: Everyman's Library, E. P. Dutton & Co., 1937

CONANT, JAMES B. (ed.), *Harvard Case Histories in Experimental Science,* 2 vols. Cambridge: Harvard University Press, 1957

COPERNICUS, *Commentariolus* in *Three Copernican Treatises.* Trans. by Edward Rosen. New York: Columbia University Press, 1939

EINSTEIN, ALBERT, *Relativity.* Trans. by Robert W. Lawson. New York: Crown Publishers, 1931

FARADAY, MICHAEL, *The Chemical History of a Candle.* New York: Thomas Y. Crowell Co., 1957

GALILEI, GALILEO, *Dialogue on the Great World Systems.* Ed. by Giorgio de Santillana. Chicago: The University of Chicago Press, 1953; *The Starry Messenger* in *Discoveries and Opinions of Galileo.* Trans. and ed. by

Stillman Drake. Garden City, N.Y.: Doubleday Anchor Books, 1957

HELMHOLTZ, HERMANN VON, *Popular Lectures on Scientific Subjects*, 2 vols. Trans. by E. Atkinson. New York: Longmans, Green and Co., 1898

KNICKERBOCKER, WM. S. (ed.), *Classics of Modern Science*. New York: Alfred A. Knopf, 1927

LEICESTER and KLICKSTEIN (ed.), *Source Book in Chemistry*. Cambridge: Harvard University Press, 1956

MACH, ERNST, *Conservation of Energy*. Trans. by P. E. B. Jourdain. Chicago: Open Court Publishing Co., 1911

MAGIE, WILLIAM, *Source Book in Physics*. New York: McGraw-Hill, 1935

MAXWELL, JAMES CLERK, *Matter and Motion*. New York: Dover Publications, 1958

SHAPLEY, H. and HOWARTH, E. H., *Source Book in Astronomy*. Cambridge: Harvard University Press, 1956

STEVIN, SIMON, *Principal Works*, Vol. 1, *Mechanics*. Ed. by E. J. Dijksterhuis, trans. by C. Dikshoorn. Amsterdam: C. V. Swets & Zeitlinger

E. Histories of Natural Science

BUTTERFIELD, HERBERT, *The Origins of Modern Science*. New York: Macmillan Co., 1957

CREW, HENRY, *The Rise of Modern Physics*. Baltimore: William and Wilkins Co., 1935

CROMBIE, A. C., *Medieval and Early Modern Science*, 2 vols. Garden City, N.Y.: Doubleday Anchor Books, 1959

EINSTEIN, ALBERT and INFELD, LEOPOLD, *The Evolution of Physics*. New York: Simon and Schuster, 1938

FARRINGTON, BENJAMIN, *Greek Science*, 2 vols. Harmondsworth, Middlesex: Penguin Books, 1949

SARTON, GEORGE, *A History of Science*. Cambridge: Harvard University Press, 1952

SINGER, CHARLES JOSEPH, *A Short History of Science*. Oxford: The Clarendon Press, 1941

The History of Science, A Symposium. Glencoe, Illinois: The Free Press, 1957

WHEWELL, WILLIAM, *History of the Inductive Sciences*, 2 vols. New York: D. Appleton and Co., 1859

WHITTAKER, SIR EDMUND, *From Euclid to Eddington*. New York: Dover Publications, Inc., 1958; *A History of the Theories of Aether and Electricity*. New York: Philosophical Library, 1951

WIENER, P. P. and NOLAND, A. (ed.), *The Roots of Scientific Thought*. New York: Basic Books, 1957

WIGHTMAN, W. P. D., *The Growth of Scientific Ideas*. New Haven: Yale University Press, 1951

WOLF, A., *A History of Science, Technology, and Philosophy in the Eighteenth Century*. London: George Allen & Unwin, Ltd. Second edition, 1952

F. Philosophy of Science and Scientific Method

BRIDGMAN, PERCY W., *The Logic of Modern Physics*. New York: Macmillan Co., 1949

BROAD, C. D., *Scientific Thought*. Paterson, N.J.: Littlefield, Adams & Co., 1959

BROGLIE, LOUIS DE, *Matter and Light*. Trans. by W. H. Johnston. New York: Dover Publications, 1946; *The Revolution in Physics*. Trans. by Ralph W. Niemeyer. New York: Noonday Press, 1958

BURTT, E. A., *The Metaphysical Foundations of Modern Science*. Garden City, N.Y.: Doubleday Anchor Books, 1954

CAMPBELL, N. R., *Physics: the Elements*. Cambridge University Press, 1920; the same book is published under the title *Foundations of Science*. New York: Dover Publications, 1957

CARNAP, RUDOLF, *The Unity of Science*. Trans. by M. Black. London: Kegan Paul, Trench, Trubner & Co., 1934

CASSIRER, ERNST, *Substance and Function* and *Einstein's Theory of Relativity*. Trans. by Wm. C. Swabey and Marie C. Swabey. New York: Dover Publications, 1953

CLIFFORD, W. K., *The Common Sense of the Exact Sciences*. New York: Dover Publications, 1955

CONANT, JAMES B., *Modern Science and Modern Man*. Garden City, N.Y.: Doubleday Anchor Books, 1955; *On Understanding Science*. New York: New American Library, 1957

DEWEY, JOHN, *Logic, The Theory of Inquiry.* New York: Henry Holt, 1938

EDDINGTON, SIR ARTHUR S., *The Nature of the Physical World.* Ann Arbor, Michigan: Ann Arbor Paperbacks, 1958; *Space, Time and Gravitation.* Cambridge: at the Cambridge University Press, 1923

EINSTEIN, ALBERT, *Sidelights on Relativity.* Trans. by G. B. Jeffery and W. Perret. New York: E. P. Dutton & Co., 1922

FEIGL, HERBERT and BRODBECK, MAY (ed.), *Readings in the Philosophy of Science.* New York: Appleton-Century-Crofts, Inc., 1953

FRANK, PHILIPP, *Between Physics and Philosophy.* Cambridge: Harvard University Press, 1941; *Foundations of Physics.* International Encyclopedia of Unified Science, Vol. 1, No. 7. Chicago: The University of Chicago Press, 1947

HEISENBERG, WERNER, *The Physicist's Conception of Nature.* Trans. by A. J. Pomerans. New York: Harcourt, Brace & Co., 1958; *Physics and Philosophy.* New York: Harper & Brothers, 1958

MACH, ERNST, *The Science of Mechanics.* Trans. by T. J. McCormack. Chicago: Open Court Publishing Co., 1942

MARGENAU, HENRY, *The Nature of Physical Reality.* New York: McGraw-Hill, 1951

MILL, J. S., *A System of Logic.* London: Longmans, Green & Co., 1952

PLANCK, MAX, *Scientific Autobiography.* Trans. by Frank Gaynor. New York: Philosophical Library, 1949; *The*

Universe in the Light of Modern Physics. Trans. by W. H. Johnston. London: George Allen & Unwin Ltd., 1937

POINCARÉ, HENRI, *The Foundations of Science (Science and Hypothesis, The Value of Science, Science and Method).* Trans. by G. B. Halsted. Lancaster, Pa.: The Science Press, 1946

REICHENBACH, HANS, *Experience and Prediction.* Chicago: University of Chicago Press, 1938; *Philosophy of Space and Time.* New York: Dover Publications; *The Rise of Scientific Philosophy.* Berkeley and Los Angeles: The University of California Press, 1951

RUSSELL, BERTRAND, *Human Knowledge, Its Scope and Limits.* New York: Simon and Schuster, 1948

SCHILPP, PAUL A. (ed.), *Albert Einstein: Philosopher-Scientist.* Evanston, Illinois: The Library of Living Philosophers, 1949; also published in 2 vols. New York: Harper Torchbooks, 1959

SCHRÖDINGER, ERWIN, *Science and Humanism.* Cambridge University Press, 1951; *What is Life?* Garden City, N.Y.: Doubleday Anchor Books, 1956

STEBBING, L. SUSAN, *Philosophy and the Physicists.* New York: Dover Publications, Inc., 1958

WHEWELL, WILLIAM, *The Philosophy of the Inductive Sciences,* 2 vols. London: J. W. Parker, 1840

WHITEHEAD, ALFRED NORTH, *Science and the Modern World.* New York: New American Library, 1958